WALCH  PUBLISHING

Daily Warm-Ups

WORLD HISTORY

Wendy Wilson

Level II

Purchasers of this book are granted the right to reproduce all pages.
This permission is limited to a single teacher, for classroom use only.

Any questions regarding this policy or requests to purchase further
reproduction rights should be addressed to:

Permissions Editor
J. Weston Walch, Publisher
321 Valley Street • P.O. Box 658
Portland, Maine 04104-0658

SGS-SFI/COC-US09/5501

1   2   3   4   5   6   7   8   9   10

ISBN 0-8251-4345-4

Copyright © 2002

J. Weston Walch, Publisher

P.O. Box 658 • Portland, Maine 04104-0658

www.walch.com

Printed in the United States of America

The *Daily Warm-Ups series* is a wonderful way to turn extra classroom minutes into valuable learning time. The 180 quick activities—one for each day of the school year—review, practice, and teach world history facts. These daily activities may be used at the very beginning of class to get students into learning mode, near the end of class to make good educational use of that transitional time, in the middle of class to shift gears between lessons—or whenever else you have minutes that now go unused. In addition to providing students with fascinating historical information, they are a natural path to other classroom activities involving critical thinking.

Daily Warm-Ups are easy-to-use reproducibles—simply photocopy the day's activity and distribute it. Or make a transparency of the activity and project it on the board. You may want to use the activities for extra-credit points or as a check on the historical and critical-thinking skills that are built and acquired over time.

However you choose to use them, *Daily Warm-Ups* are a convenient and useful supplement to your regular lesson plans. Make every minute of your class time count!

Louis Leakey and Zinjanthropus

One afternoon in 1959, **anthropologist** Mary Leakey was walking in Olduvai Gorge, Tanzania. Her husband and partner, Louis, lay in his tent with a fever. Suddenly, in the slanting sunlight, Mary saw a piece of a **hominid** jawbone. This proved to be the creature they had been seeking for 28 years. They named it Zinjanthropus.

What was the significance of the Leakeys' find? Why did it startle the scientific community and lead toward a new direction in analyzing the history of early humans?

Shanidar Cave

An important **Neanderthal** burial site is the Shanidar Cave in northern Iraq. One Neanderthal skeleton found there was of a man who had been seriously disabled by a birth defect.

How do you think this man was able to reach adulthood in his community? What does this tell us about Neanderthals' level of humanity?

2

Fred Flintstone

Believe it or not, the cartoon character Fred Flintstone represents a breakthrough in the history of human development. Scientists found "flint stones" in caves that had been inhabited by Neanderthals. From this, they knew that these ancestors to modern humans had achieved an important step in history.

What was this step? How did it enable Neanderthals to progress over previous human forerunners?

3

Female Farmers

During the **Neolithic Revolution,** around 6000 B.C.E., women were the primary breadwinners. As game grew scarce and reliance on crops grew, the men continued to hunt. They were often unsuccessful. Meanwhile, women planted grain and other domesticated plants.

When did this role reversal end and the more "traditional" gender roles begin?

4

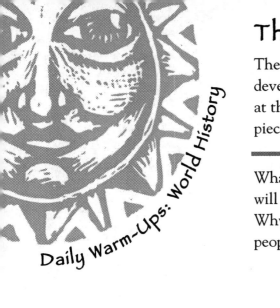

The Importance of Pottery

The ability to make pottery was an important technological development in early human societies. When **archaeologists** dig at the site of an early human community, they find many pottery pieces known as **shards.**

What remains of our civilization do you think archaeologists will find hundreds or even thousands of years from now? Why is archaeology sometimes described as "looking at other people's garbage"?

5

© 2002 J. Weston Walch, Publisher

Jericho

The first town that we know about from **excavation** is Jericho, in modern-day Jordan. Jericho was settled by 7000 B.C.E. It was rebuilt many times in its long history. The walls were 15 feet high, and there was a stone tower about 25 feet high. The people of Jericho were farmers, but they also traded and hunted.

What geographical features would you look for if you were planning to build a town starting from scratch? How did Jericho's location match up with the features you identified?

6

The *Epic of Gilgamesh*

The *Epic of Gilgamesh* is the earliest known **epic** poem.

Written in Sumer perhaps as early as 3000 B.C.E., the poem tells the story of a god–hero, Gilgamesh, and his quest to escape death and achieve immortality. One section of this epic tells of Utnapishtim. The gods tell Utnapishtim to build a boat and take with him his family and "the seed of all living things." They will escape a flood that will wipe out all life on earth.

Have you heard another version of this story? What does the appearance of this story in other cultures tell us about communication between early Middle Eastern and Mediterranean cultures?

7

Mummies

One of the strangest fads in seventeenth-century Europe was the desire for mummy powder. This was made from the bodies of mummified Egyptians. Mummy powder was supposed to be a cure for many ills—broken bones, headaches, ulcers, liver disorders, and rashes. The demand for this powder caused many mummies to be brought from Egypt and destroyed.

Why was the craze for mummy medicine so damaging to our knowledge of Egypt? What can modern scientists learn from mummies?

8

Daily Warm-Ups: World History

The Valley of the Kings

Due to the ransacking of the royal burials in the pyramids, after about 1500 B.C.E., royal tombs were moved to the Valley of the Kings. This was an isolated area in the hills beyond Thebes. A community of workers labored on the royal tombs for 420 years. Even in this remote place, however, grave robbers sought out the riches of the tombs. Most of the burial chambers were opened and robbed. Except one.

What was this famous tomb of a minor eighteenth-dynasty pharaoh that was discovered almost totally intact in 1922? What was the significance of this discovery?

9

© 2002 J. Weston Walch, Publisher

An Urban Puzzle

These two ancient cities were probably the best examples of urban planning until the twentieth century. Streets were laid out in a grid pattern. There was a sophisticated water supply and sewage removal system, which included indoor plumbing.

What were these two great cities that existed around 2500 B.C.E. in what is modern-day Pakistan?

10

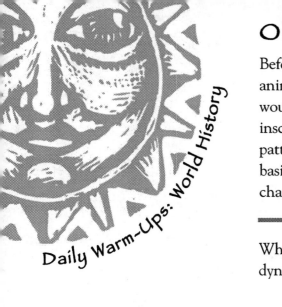

Oracle Bones

Before the Shang dynasty, the Chinese used cracks formed in animal bones and shells to make prophecies. Priests or shamans would interpret these "oracle bones." Later, the bones were inscribed with designs. These designs were incorporated into the patterns read by the shamans. Eventually these designs became the basis for Chinese writing. This complex system had almost 3,000 characters by the end of the Shang dynasty.

What other characteristics of a river valley civilization did Shang dynasty China (c. 1500 B.C.E.) develop?

11

The Importance of the Horse

When **agriculture** first began in the Middle East and Africa, horses were unknown. Oxen were the principal mode of transportation. They were also used to plow fields. Horses were found in the wild on the steppes of central Asia. The Indo-European peoples who lived there tamed and used the horse. When the Indo-Europeans invaded the civilized areas of southwest Asia, the horse-drawn chariot was a fearsome weapon. As people learned the use of the horse and the chariot, new groups of warriors would venture forth to conquer new territory.

Did anything beneficial come from this warfare and movement of peoples that began around 1000 B.C.E.?

12

Famous Archaeologists

Match each archaeologist on the left with his or her most famous site or discovery on the right.

1. Howard Carter

2. Max Mallowan

3. Arthur Evans

4. Sir Flinders Petrie

5. Kathleen Kenyon

(a) Ceramic chronology dating technique

(b) King Tut's Tomb

(c) Jericho

(d) Nineveh (Assyrian culture)

(e) Palace of Knossos on Crete

Bonus question: Max Mallowan's wife was a famous writer who went with her husband on archaeological digs. She often included her adventures in her mystery books. Who was she?

13

Hammurabi's Code

Hammurabi, the king of Babylon (c. 1800–1750 B.C.E.), united Mesopotamia under his rule. Hammurabi's law code, although probably based upon earlier Sumerian models, is the earliest **codification** of law that we have.

From the examples of laws given, what can you tell about Mesopotamian society?

- If a man has accused a man and has charged him with manslaughter and then has not proved it against him, the accuser will be put to death.

- If a man has committed robbery and is caught, that man shall be put to death.

- If a son strikes his father, his forehand shall be cut off.

- If a builder has built a house for a man, and his work is not strong, and if the house he has built falls in and kills the householder, that builder shall be slain.

14

Who Am I?

I began my reign as an Egyptian pharaoh in c. 1379 B.C.E. I am one of the most controversial leaders in the ancient world. This is because I tried to change the traditional **polytheistic** religion of Egypt to the worship of one god, Aten. Portraits show me as deformed, with an elongated head, spindly legs, and a sagging belly. Modern scientists argue over whether this was evidence of a glandular disorder or whether I ordered artists to show me this way. Artwork was very different during my reign—more naturalistic and less stylized. After my death, the religion went back to the way it had been. My royal pictures and inscriptions were often defaced in an attempt to rid Egypt of the memory of the "heretic" pharaoh.

Who am I?

15

Where Am I?

I am about 25 feet above the ground on this great structure, which is 12 feet wide and stretches for 1,500 miles. As I look to the west, I scan the horizon for any approach of the enemy. I am confident that the soldiers in the guardhouse over the next hill will also be alert. We must not allow the barbarian to enter the Middle Kingdom.

Where am I?

Minoans—Mystery People of the Aegean Area

Around 2000 B.C.E., a rich and vibrant culture developed on the island of Crete. This culture is called Minoan after the legendary King Minos. According to the Greeks, Minos lived on Crete. The Minoans built sophisticated palaces and created artwork of great beauty. However, we do not know where they came from. Their own writing, known as Linear A, remains undeciphered. Another type of writing found on Crete was determined to be an early form of Greek. Largely used for inventories of goods, this script tells us something about Crete's position geographically, economically, and culturally in the world of the eastern Mediterranean.

In a clear paragraph, explain the significance of this early civilization and why the Minoans are often considered the precursors to the Greek civilization.

17

Zoroastrianism

The people of the Persian Empire were Indo-Europeans. In their earliest period, they had a **polytheistic** religion like the Aryans of India. In the sixth century B.C.E., the religion of Persia changed due to the teachings of Zoroaster or Zarathustra. Zarathustra taught that there was a supreme god of goodness and light—Ahura Mazda—and an evil, destructive spirit—Angra Mainya or Ahriman. In the future there would be a struggle between the forces of good and evil. Humans would be judged upon the basis of whether they chose to do good or evil. Moral individuals would enter a heavenly afterlife, but evil ones would be punished with pain and suffering. Zarathustra's teachings were popular in Persia for hundreds of years. His influence declined after the introduction of Islam in the seventh century C.E.

18

Persia was a cosmopolitan empire that influenced many other cultures. What characteristics of Zoroastrianism affected other religions?

Who Said This?

According to this famous sixth century B.C.E. Chinese scholar, a good man is a person who:

> Treats his betters as betters,
> Wears an air of respect,
> Who in serving father and mother
> Knows how to put in his whole strength,
> Who in the service of his prince will lay down his life,
> Who in intercourse with friends is true to his word.

Who said this?

Religious Leader Matchup

Match each religious leader on the left with the religion or concept on the right that he is connected with.

1. Moses
2. Lao-tse
3. Mahavira
4. Gautama Siddhartha
5. Zarathustra

(a) Buddhism
(b) renewed covenant with Yahweh and the Hebrews
(c) Zoroastrianism
(d) Daoism (Taoism)
(e) Jainism

20

An Elephant in Every House?

The elephant has held an important position in Indian tradition for thousands of years. According to Indian belief, the wife of the great god Shiva produced a son from her own sweat and named him Ganesha. Ganesha was to guard his mother's door. When he denied entrance to Shiva, the god had Ganesha's head cut off. His mother searched around for a suitable replacement and found a baby elephant's head. Ganesha, the elephant-headed god, is considered a remover of obstacles and a bringer of good fortune. Many homes and businesses in India have a statue of Ganesha.

In one clear paragraph, explain the difference between Hinduism, India's oldest religion, and Buddhism, a religion founded in the sixth century B.C.E.

21

The Riddle of Judah

This small, seemingly insignificant kingdom was conquered ruthlessly by the Babylonian King Nebuchadnezzar in 586 B.C.E. It had taken Nebuchadnezzar two years to starve out the inhabitants of Judah's capital city. He was quick to torch the royal palace and temple. Much of the population of Judah was sent into exile to Babylon. It was hoped that they would become assimilated into the population there.

What happened to these people? Were they assimilated? What major contribution do we owe to the inhabitants of Judah that is still in existence today?

22

The Army of Qin Shihuangdi

One of the most amazing archaeological finds of the twentieth century was the terra-cotta army of China's first emperor, Qin Shihuangdi (reigned 221–210 B.C.E.). Part of the extravagant tomb built by as many as 700,000 laborers, the terra-cotta army contained thousands of life-size, highly detailed clay figures of warriors. The warriors had individualized faces. They represented such varied military roles as infantrymen, commanding officers, charioteers (complete with terra-cotta horses), and archers.

The first emperor was a ruthless man who ruled with an iron fist. Some of his accomplishments set the precedent for a centralized and unified China. What were they?

23

Importance of the Polis

For ancient Greeks, nothing was as important as their **city-state,** or **polis.** According to the Greeks, to be human you had to reside in a *polis* and be part of its life. Each *polis* had a marketplace, or *agora*.

What words in the English language do we get from *polis* and *agora*?

24

Alexander the Great

What was purple and conquered the world? Alexander the Grape!
The basis of this terrible joke was in reality a great conqueror
and a remarkable person. Educated by the Athenian philosopher
Aristotle, Alexander is considered very controversial. He has been
seen by historians as a figure to praise or a figure to scorn.

Divide a sheet of paper into two columns. List the positive
accomplishments of Alexander on one side and his negative deeds
on the other. In your opinion, which side weighs more heavily?

25

© 2002 J. Weston Walch, Publisher

Julius Caesar and the Calendar

One of Julius Caesar's accomplishments as **dictator** of Rome was to reform the Roman calendar. This calendar was widely used until it was replaced by the Gregorian calendar in the late sixteenth century C.E.

Which names of months came from Caesar's time, and what are their origins?

26

Rome, an Urban Empire

From northern Britain to Jordan, Roman ruins are everywhere in Europe, North Africa, and the Middle East. At its height, Rome was an urban empire, one that was based on the culture of the city. Roman cities were centers of law, trade, education, and culture. London, England, began as a Roman military outpost.

What characteristics did most Roman cities share? What **infrastructure** did the Romans create for their cities?

27

The Silk Route

In this day of rapid air travel, when we go to the supermarket we can find melons from Israel, plums from Chile, cheese from France, and spices from India. Two thousand years ago, travel was obviously not as rapid or as effortless. One of the most extensive communication and transportation networks was the silk route. The silk route or silk road was actually a meshed system of trading routes connecting China with the Byzantine Empire. Spanning 7,000 miles over some of the most challenging terrain in the world, the silk roads carried goods, people, and ideas from Asia to Europe and in reverse.

28

What goods were carried along the silk roads? What cultural ideas and other intangible things might be carried along with physical items?

The Legacy of Saul of Tarsus

Saul of Tarsus, known in the Christian tradition as St. Paul, is often considered the true founder of Christianity as a world religion. Saul combined three important attributes: he was a Roman citizen, he was from a city that was a center of Greek culture, and he was Jewish. Saul started out as a persecutor of the early followers of Jesus. He was on his way to Damascus to pursue Christians there when he had a mystical religious experience. This experience caused him to become a Christian himself.

What were Saul's contributions to the early Christian Church?

29

© 2002 J. Weston Walch, Publisher

Corn in Meso-America

Corn is a plant that is indigenous to the Americas. It is currently believed that corn was first cultivated in Meso-America, probably Mexico, as early as 3500 B.C.E. Its use spread through the American continents. Originally corn was a small grain; each "ear" was about the size of a Tootsie Roll. Corn offered a large yield for relatively little labor.

Why was this important for the early civilizations that developed in Meso-America? What things did it enable their populations to do with their time?

30

Riddle of the Fall of Rome

The Germanic tribes that conquered Rome had no concept of such things as Roman law and justice. The believed in trial by ordeal. When accused of a crime the defendant had to undergo an ordeal such as thrusting his hand into a fire or holding a red-hot iron bar. If the wound healed, he was innocent. If it became gangrenous, he was guilty (and would probably die anyway!).

How could these "uncivilized" barbarians overrun and destroy one of the greatest empires the world had known? Was it the strength of the Germanic tribes, or was it the weakness of the Roman Empire after c. 200 C.E., that caused the fall of the Roman Empire?

31

Justinian

Justinian (527–565 C.E.) was known as the "emperor who never slept." With his strong-willed empress, Theodora, he tried to bring back the power and glory of the Roman Empire. Instead, he laid the foundations of the **Byzantine Empire,** which was centered around the city of Constantinople.

List the accomplishments of Justinian.

32

The Koran

To Muslims, the Koran is the word of God as it was revealed to Muhammad and later copied down. To Muslims, the Koran represents the final revelation. Muhammad is viewed as the last and greatest of all the prophets. Many of the Jewish prophets are mentioned in the Koran. So is Jesus, who is regarded as a prophet, not a divinity.

What are some of the differences between the Bible and the Koran?

33

© 2002 J. Weston Walch, Publisher

Where Am I?

I am standing in the courtyard of the Great Mosque. I can see in the center of the courtyard the large square building called the Kaaba. On the outside corner of the Kaaba is the sacred black stone, given to Ishmael by the angel Gabriel. Hundreds of pilgrims crowd toward the Kaaba to reverently kiss the black stone as part of their *hajj*, or pilgrimage.

Where am I?

34

Baghdad

One of the most sophisticated and opulent cities in the world during the ninth century was Baghdad, home of the Abbasid dynasty. This was the city of Aladdin captured in the tales of *The Thousand and One Nights*, a place of vibrant culture, trade, and commerce. Merchants were very important in this rich urban culture.

Contrast this culture with conditions in western Europe at the same time.

35

Polynesia

Between 1500 B.C.E. and 1000 C.E., the ancestors of people we call the Polynesians settled islands in the Pacific east of the Asian mainland. The area referred to as Polynesia includes the islands in an imaginary triangle that runs from the Hawaiian Islands to the north, Easter Island to the east, and New Zealand to the south. Although these people developed cultures pretty much in isolation from each other, when Captain Cook explored the area in the eighteenth century he found that people in these island groups spoke a similar language. Words from Tahiti were understood in Hawaii even though the islands were 2,500 miles apart.

What does this tell us about the origin of these island peoples?

36

Mayan Cities

Throughout Central America, and particularly in the Yucatán area of Mexico, hundreds and hundreds of Mayan archaeological sites are found. Remains of houses, walls, pyramids, and temples are being uncovered from the dense vegetation.

Classical Mayan culture (c. 300–800 C.E.) was a densely populated urban culture. But were the Maya a civilization? What characteristics of a civilization did the Mayas possess? What characteristics did they lack?

37

Ruler Matchup

Match each ruler on the left (c. 300–1000 C.E.) with the correct Asian country on the right.

1. Chandragupta
2. Dinh Bo Linh
3. Suryavarmann II
4. Fujiwara emperors
5. Tang Taizong

(a) Vietnam
(b) Khmer Kingdom (Cambodia)
(c) India
(d) China
(e) Japan

38

What Is This Kingdom?

Located in the savanna area of Africa, between the gold-producing area of the Niger and Senegal river valleys and the sands of the Sahara Desert, this kingdom developed as a state during the fifth and sixth centuries C.E. As Muslim merchants from North Africa exploited and expanded trade routes across the Sahara, by the ninth century C.E., this kingdom was the chief supplier of gold to the Mediterranean world. The Muslim scholar al-Bakri wrote a description of this kingdom in 1067 C.E., which gives us an idea of its power and richness.

What was this kingdom called?

39

The Role of the Pope

In the early Christian Church, many bishops, claiming to be the successors of the apostles, had power over believers. By the fifth century C.E., the bishops of Rome began to claim that they had power over all other bishops. They took the title "pope" from the Latin word for father and claimed exclusive right to be the head of the Church.

Upon what theory did popes claim this right? How did this ultimately cause a split or **schism** in Christianity in 1054 C.E.?

40

A "Schoolhouse for the Lord"

One of the most important institutions to develop in the early Middle Ages was **monasticism.** This was the practice of men and women who lived apart from the rest of the world in communities dedicated to serving God. Benedict of Nursia and his twin sister Scholastica helped establish communal monasticism after the fall of Rome. Benedict wrote a "Rule" that set out the way monks and nuns should live their lives. Benedict did not think people should live as hermits and wandering holy men. He thought that people who wished to devote their lives to God should live in obedience to their rule and spend their time balanced between work and prayer. Benedict called monasteries a "schoolhouse for the Lord."

List some of the contributions of monasteries to medieval culture.

41

Charlemagne

When Charlemagne went to church in Rome on Christmas Day in the year 800 C.E., he did not expect the pope to place a crown on his head and name him emperor. But it happened! As emperor, Charlemagne embodied the close relationship between religion and politics that characterized medieval Europe.

Using the PRIMES approach (**p**olitical, **r**eligious, **i**ntellectual, **m**ilitary, **e**conomic, and **s**ocial), list one contribution of Charlemagne's reign in each category.

42

Vikings

Chronicles written by European monks of the ninth and tenth centuries implore God to "save us from the wrath of the Northmen." Coastal areas and lands along estuaries and rivers were particularly vulnerable to attack by the **Vikings.** The Vikings or Northmen seemed absolutely unstoppable. However, on the west coast of Scotland, they seemingly met their match. In 1263, at the town of Largs, a group of Scots, led by King Alexander III of Scotland, drove the Vikings off. This is celebrated as a great Scottish victory. Today, even the movie theater in Largs is shaped like a Viking longboat.

Why were the Vikings on the move during this time period? What were they seeking? Where did they eventually settle?

43

Chang'an and the Tang Dynasty

The capital city of the Tang dynasty (617–907 C.E.) was Chang'an. At its peak, as many as one million people lived within the city's walls. Chang'an was laid out in an organized grid pattern. It was divided into wards, which were enclosed within internal walls and gated. Each night the main city and the wards were locked.

The Tang dynasty established an important governmental pattern that lasted for a thousand years. What were the main features of this governmental pattern?

44

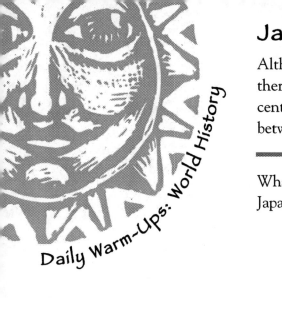

Japan and China

Although the Japanese archipelago lies off the Asian mainland, there was contact between Japan and other Asian cultures for centuries. By the fourth century C.E., there was extensive contact between Japan and China.

What were the results of this contact? What cultural elements did Japan learn from China?

45

1066

1066 is a date that every English schoolchild knows by heart. It is considered one of the pivotal dates in British history.

In one clear sentence, why is this date so important?

46

A Formidable Woman

Eleanor of Aquitane was not the typical medieval maiden. Married at fifteen to King Louis VII of France, she went with him on a **crusade** to the Holy Land. When Eleanor did not have a son, Louis had their marriage declared invalid in 1152. Within two months Eleanor married Henry, the Duke of Normandy. Henry became King Henry II of England. He and Eleanor had eight children, two of whom became kings of England (Richard I and John). As Henry grew older, he was unfaithful to his wife. Eleanor retaliated by joining her sons in a war against Henry. Henry put Eleanor under "house arrest" in a castle. After Henry died in 1189, Eleanor was released from confinement. She was left in charge of England while Richard, her favorite son, went off on a crusade.

Despite Eleanor's power, riches, and marriages, we know very little about her. We do not even have a contemporary description of her appearance. Why?

47

A Terrible King

No other king in English history has taken this king's name as ruler. He angered the pope, who placed England under an **interdict** that shut all the churches. He lost much English-controlled territory in France. And his barons took arms against him at Runnymede and forced him to sign the Magna Carta in 1215.

Who was this terrible king?

48

Medieval Matchup

Match each term on the left with the correct definition on the right.

1. fief

2. homage and fealty

3. chivalry

4. serf

5. corvée

6. grant of immunity

7. manor

(a) a fortified, self-sufficient farm

(b) a laborer who is bound to the land of his manor

(c) three days' worth of labor owed to the lord of a manor by a peasant

(d) the code of honor of the knightly class

(e) a gift of land given by a lord to his vassal in return for military service

(f) a ceremony where a vassal pledges loyalty to his lord

(g) the right received by a vassal to govern his land as he wishes

49

© 2002 J. Weston Walch, Publisher

Medieval Universities

"Well-beloved father, I have not a penny, nor can I get any save through you, for all things at the University are so dear: nor can I study in my Code or my Digest, for they are all tattered. Moreover, I owe ten crowns in dues to the Provost, and find no man to lend them to me; I send you word of greetings and money. The student hath need of many things if he will profit here; his father and his kin must needs supply him freely that he be not compelled to pawn his books, but have ready money in his purse with gowns and furs and decent clothing, or he will be damned for a beggar; wherefore that men may not take me for a beast, I send you word of greetings and of money."

50

This letter was written by a student at a medieval university to his father. How does this letter show that medieval students had some things in common with university students today? How were medieval universities different from ours?

The Crusades

In 1291, the last crusader outpost in the Middle East fell. Christians in the Holy Land paid any amount of money to book passage on ships back to western Europe. What had begun in 1096 as a glorious mission to recapture the Holy Land for Christianity ended in defeat.

List the results of the Crusades for history.

The Black Death

It started with aching joints, a fever, and swollen lymph nodes, which might turn black. Sometimes the lungs were affected and the victim coughed and sneezed. Whatever the symptoms, the disease progressed quickly, death was almost always swift, and it spread rapidly from person to person. This was the **bubonic plague,** or Black Death. It swept through Europe in the mid-fourteenth century, killing one-third to one-half of the population. In many cases, bodies lay in the streets, with no one to perform burials. Since medical and scientific knowledge was too primitive to explain the disease rationally, people sought strange remedies. They often took revenge on the innocent in their quest to get rid of the plague. People known as **flagellants** whipped themselves to appease God. Others persecuted the Jews to find a scapegoat for their misery.

52

What were the economic results of the number of people killed by the plague?

Holy Roman Empire

It was not holy, not Roman, and not an empire in the true sense. Still, this huge territory dominated parts of western and central Europe from the early Middle Ages until it was dissolved by Napoleon.

What modern-day European states did the Holy Roman Empire include?

Henry the Navigator

On the cliffs above the ocean at Sagres, Portugal, stand the remains of a huge compass carved in the soil and marked with stones. This was part of Prince Henry (1394–1469) of Portugal's school of navigation and exploration. Henry, known as the Navigator for his interest in exploration, encouraged Portuguese exploration to find a route to the Indian Ocean and India. Europeans wished to avoid the high prices charged by the Ottoman Turks for eastern goods.

What route did Henry encourage to reach India? When was that route finally discovered and successfully completed? How did Portugal's rival in exploration, Spain, propose to reach India and the Indies?

54

The Spanish Inquisition

King Ferdinand and Queen Isabella of Spain were extremely devout Catholics. They were referred to as "Their Catholic Majesties." In their desire to seek out people who were secretly practicing Judaism or Islam, the monarchs received a license from the pope to operate the **Spanish Inquisition** as an arm of the state. Under the dreaded chief inquisitor Torquemada, the court was ruthless. Victims were often chosen for their political views as well as religious **heresy.** Although the Inquisition operated as a court of law and some people were released because the charges were not proven, hundreds were tortured and burned at the stake, usually in a public display.

What was the result of this for Spain?

55

© 2002 J. Weston Walch, Publisher

Fall of Constantinople, 1453

Constantinople was first attacked by Islamic armies as early as 677. Although the Byzantine Empire was able to continue on for hundreds of years, a new group of nomads from Asia who began to move to the west were to spell its doom. Known as the Saljuq Turks, these people had been converted to Islam. They were ruled by men called **sultans** who believed that they were the successors to Muhammad. Under Sultan Mehmed II, Constantinople was attacked by land and sea. It fell in 1453. The old Byzantine Empire was now ruled by Muslims. It came to be known as the **Ottoman Empire.**

List three consequences of this for western Europe.

56

Who Was He?

This man said on his deathbed in 1324 in Venice, "I have not told you the half of what I had experienced because I knew you would not believe me." Today it is believed that many of his tales were false or greatly exaggerated.

Who was he?

57

Who Am I?

I was a Muslim who commanded a grand expedition from China between 1405 and 1433 to explore the Indian Ocean. My first voyage had 317 ships with 28,000 armed soldiers. Many of the vessels were "treasure ships." They had four decks that could carry huge amounts of cargo, even floating gardens. At every port I called, I expected my hosts to show respect and obedience to the power of China. I usually commanded respect by using tact and diplomacy. I showered those I visited with gifts from China. I brought back zebras, giraffes, and ostriches from Africa for the Ming imperial zoo. My voyages came to nought when the Ming emperors decided to stop the expeditions. The maps I had prepared were destroyed. China never followed up on my great expeditions, unlike the Europeans, who were about to embark on great voyages of discovery.

Who am I?

The Golden Horde

During the thirteenth century, the nomadic peoples of central Asia played a huge role in history. The most dominant group was the **Mongols,** originally led by a warrior who took the name Chinggis Khan (Genghis Khan).

One group of Mongols was the **Golden Horde,** named after the golden tent of their leader. The Golden Horde dominated Russia. They treated it as a vassal state, exacting tribute payments until the mid-fifteenth century. At that time, the princes of Muscovy (Moscow) began to build a Russian nation. They renounced the authority of the Mongol **khans** (leaders).

What other areas of Asia did the Mongols come to dominate?

59

© 2002 J. Weston Walch, Publisher

Japanese Feudalism

At the same time that feudalism was developing in western Europe, it also developed in Japan. Japanese warriors were known as **samurai.** They practiced a military ethic known as "the way of the bow and the horse." Samurai believed in death before dishonor. They practiced a ritual suicide called **seppuku** (disembowelment) if they were defeated or disgraced.

How was feudalism in Japan different from feudalism in western Europe?

60

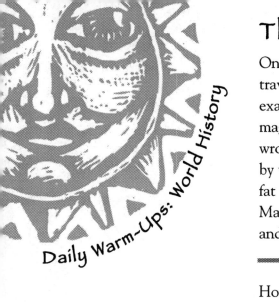

The Travels of John Mandeville

One of the most popular books in the late medieval period was a travel book written by a knight named Sir John Mandeville. Who exactly was he? No one really knows, but his tales of strange and magical lands caught the imagination of many readers. Mandeville wrote about traveling to the land of Amazonia, totally inhabited by women. He wrote of cannibals who raised children to be fat and boasted of the sweetness of the flesh of such children. Mandeville also wrote of a legendary king, Prester John, a wealthy and powerful Christian king in India.

How might reports like these influence the early explorers as they reached new lands?

61

Mansa Musa (1312–1337)

My name was Mansa Kankan Musa. I reigned as king in the early fourteenth century in a kingdom known for controlling most of the trans-Saharan trade. Huge caravans with as many as 25,000 camels connected my kingdom to North Africa. Since I was a Muslim, it was my duty to make a *hajj*, or **pilgrimage,** to Mecca in 1324. My retinue was huge, with thousands of soldiers, slaves, officials, and subjects. Everywhere I traveled I gave gifts to my hosts. I gave away so much gold that it went down in value in that region. I brought back to my kingdom from Mecca a famous poet and architect, Ishak al-Sahili, to help build mosques and other buildings.

What was the name of my kingdom?

62

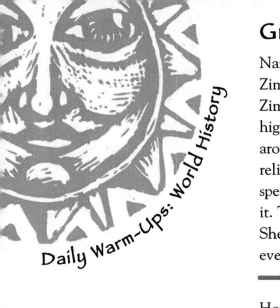

Great Zimbabwe

Named a World Heritage site by UNESCO in 1986, Great Zimbabwe is a huge stone structure in the modern nation of Zimbabwe. This 800-foot-long structure has outer walls 32 feet high and 17 feet thick in some places. It was probably started around 1200 C.E. It is thought that Great Zimbabwe was a religious, governmental, and ceremonial center for the Bantu-speaking Shona people; as many as 20,000 people lived around it. The Portuguese were sure that it was built by the Queen of Sheba. Other people felt it was built by Egyptians, Greeks, or even aliens from outer space.

How has a structure like Great Zimbabwe changed our notion about sub-Saharan Africa before Europeans arrived?

Inca Pachacuti (1438–1471)

In 1438, as the capital city of Cuzco came under attack, the son of the aging Inca seized control and repulsed the invaders. His name was Pachacuti. Forcing his father to abdicate, he became the Inca and ruled from 1438–1471. Under Pachacuti, the Incas built a huge empire. It stretched for over 2,500 miles along the west coast of South America and included 11.5 million people. The Incas ruled with the aid of a strong military and a bureaucracy. They had an excellent road system that tied their vast empire together.

What two aspects or inventions of civilization did the Incas lack? How did they deal with this?

64

Description of Human Sacrifice

". . . after they had danced they placed them on their backs on some rather narrow stones which had been prepared as places for sacrifice, and with stone knives they sawed open their chests and drew out their palpitating hearts and offered them to the idols that were there . . . ."

This may sound like a scene from a horror movie or *Indiana Jones and the Temple of Doom*, but it is a real eyewitness account of a human sacrifice. Can you guess where this is? The practice of human sacrifice was to have grave consequences for the survival of this people after c. 1500. Why?

65

Importance of Sugar

Muslims first introduced European crusaders to sugar made from sugarcane. Europeans were immediately hooked on the sweet stuff, which was more convenient as a sweetener than fruit or honey. Sugarcane grew in North Africa and Italian merchants set up sugarcane plantations on Mediterranean islands like Crete, Cyprus, and Sicily. Europeans also found that sugarcane grew well in the New World, particularly on the islands of the Caribbean. Harvesting sugar was hard and often dangerous work. Europeans found the demand for sugar high, but their labor market low.

What did they do to create a financial balance in their favor?

66

Renaissance Artists Matchup

Match each Renaissance artist on the left with the name of his masterpiece on the right.

1. Michelangelo

2. Leonardo da Vinci

3. Sandro Botticelli

4. Raphael

5. Donatello

(a) *The Birth of Venus* (painting)

(b) *The School of Athens* (painting)

(c) Sistine Chapel ceiling (painting)

(d) *St. George* (statue)

(e) *The Last Supper* (painting)

67

Lorenzo Valla, Humanist Scholar

There is probably no better example of a Renaissance humanist scholar than Lorenzo Valla (1407–1457). Valla knew both Latin and Greek. He researched classical texts to find a more pure translation than the medieval commentaries on these documents. One of his most famous achievements was to prove that the Donation of Constantine was a forgery because the Latin was written 400 years after Constantine's death. This document gave the pope territorial claims in Italy that he held until the nineteenth century. Valla's investigation of the Vulgate (the only authorized Bible at that time) inspired Erasmus to study the original Greek New Testament and correct errors found in the Vulgate.

Daily Warm-Ups: World History

68

In two or three sentences, how did humanism change the notion of scholarship as it was found in the Middle Ages?

Who Am I?

A native of Rotterdam, I was a cosmopolitan figure who corresponded with popes, emperors, kings, and scholars. Known as the "Prince of Christian Humanists," I saw the new scholarship of the Renaissance as invigorating the Christian Church. I never wavered in my loyalty to the church, even though I often criticized the bad morals and learning of the clergy. My most famous work was a satire titled *In Praise of Folly*.

Who am I?

69

© 2002 J. Weston Walch, Publisher

Mortality in the New World

The Spanish were cruel to the indigenous peoples they found in the Americas. The Dominican friar Bartolomé de Las Casas wrote that the Spanish committed acts "more irrational and ferocious than any inflicted by the most ferocious lions and tigers and rabid wolves." However, although the Spaniards committed many murders, these deaths don't account for the high mortality rate in the Americas.

What caused millions of Amerindians to die as the Europeans arrived in the New World?

70

The Potato

The New World changed the diets of Europeans, Africans, and Asians forever. One of the most popular new foods was the potato. Easy to grow, harvest, and store, the potato was a nutritious addition to the diet of the European peasant, which usually consisted of gruel and coarse bread. Ireland and areas of Scotland came to subsist almost totally on the potato. This caused a disaster when a disease hit the Irish potato crop in the 1840s.

What other common foods came from the New World to the tables of the Old World?

71

© 2002 J. Weston Walch, Publisher

Johannes Tetzel

The favorite jingle of Dominican friar Johannes Tetzel was:

> As soon as the coin in the coffer rings,
>
> Right then the soul to heaven springs.

What was Tetzel selling?

Protestant Strongholds

Match each country on the left with the Protestant religion on the right that became associated with it. (You may use a religion twice.)

1. Scotland
2. Netherlands
3. England
4. Scandinavia
5. Germany

(a) Anglican

(b) Presbyterian (Calvinist)

(c) Reformed (Calvinist)

(d) Lutheran

73

Divorced, Beheaded, Died

Divorced, beheaded, died

divorced, beheaded, survived.

To what, or to whom, does this little poem refer?

74

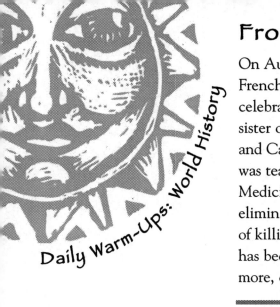

From Wedding Reception to Massacre

On August 24, 1572, the feast of St. Bartholomew, thousands of French Calvinists known as **Huguenots** were in Paris. They were celebrating the wedding of the Protestant Henry of Navarre to the sister of the king of France. This wedding was to unite the Protestant and Catholic parties in France and end the sectarian warfare that was tearing the country apart. The queen mother, Catherine de Medici, had other ideas. She persuaded the young king to order the elimination of all the Huguenot leaders. Mobs took over in a frenzy of killing. Between 2,000 and 3,000 Huguenots were killed in what has become known as the St. Bartholomew's Day Massacre. Once more, civil war broke out in France.

What finally happened in the French wars of religion to establish peace and tranquility?

75

© 2002 J. Weston Walch, Publisher

The Spanish Armada

As the Great Armada Católica set sail from Spain in the spring of 1588, the commander, Medina Sidonia, was concerned. The water and other supplies stored in the wooden casks on board the ships were spoiling. Many of the casks were defective. The English privateer Sir Francis Drake had raided Spain the year before and had burned many barrels intended for the armada supplies. New casks were built, but the staves were not seasoned wood. This caused leaks and spoilage. The Armada seemed doomed from the beginning.

What was the result of the Spanish Armada, both immediately and in the long run?

76

Lost Colony of Roanoke

In 1587, the English tried to settle a colony in the New World. The land was named "Virginia" after Queen Elizabeth I, the virgin queen. A group of men, women, and children landed on Roanoke Island in what is now North Carolina. There they tried to set up England's first permanent colony. When the colony ran short on supplies, the governor of the colony went back to England for provisions. His return trip to America was delayed. When he finally made it to Roanoke Island, the colony had disappeared. To this day we do not know what happened to the "Lost Colony of Roanoke."

England's first attempt at an American colony failed. Another country already had a colony in North America. Which country was it? Where was the colony?

77

Defenestration of Prague

In 1618, the Protestant nobles of Bohemia were in nearly open rebellion against the Holy Roman Emperor, the upholder of Catholicism within his realm. To demonstrate their disdain for royal authority, the Protestants threw two of the king's advisers out of the third-floor window of a building. Fortunately, no one was killed: the advisers landed in an enormous pile of horse manure in the courtyard. This so-called "Defenestration of Prague" led to the Thirty Years' War, the last and most destructive of the wars of religion.

78

What were the background causes to the wars of religion? What were the results of these devastating wars?

Small but Mighty

Its leaders were known as the High Mightinesses. Although not officially unified, the provinces of this republic tended to work together under the leadership of a Stadholder. The presence of this small republic was felt everywhere in the world during the seventeenth and early eighteenth centuries. Excellent businessmen and shipbuilders, the citizens of this solidly middle-class country ruled the seas until they were surpassed by the English.

Who were they?

79

Poodles into Battle?

The commander of the Royalist cavalry forces during the English Civil War was King Charles I's nephew, Prince Rupert of the Rhine. Prince Rupert had a poodle named "Boye," which he carried with him everywhere, including onto the battlefield. Surely a poodle was not the Royalists' secret weapon!

Why were the Royalists or Cavaliers so successful in the initial phases of the civil war? How were the Parliamentary forces able to take the advantage in the later part of the war?

80

Glorious Revolution

In 1688, the English chased out King James II and offered the crown to a Dutchman known as William of Orange. King William III ruled jointly with his English wife, Mary—the first time in English history that husband and wife ruled together as equals. This event was known as the Glorious Revolution.

Why exactly was it "glorious"?

81

© 2002 J. Weston Walch, Publisher

Who Am I?

I became the ruler of my country in 1682 when I was only ten years old. I grew to be six feet seven inches tall and developed a strong will and a desire for action. I traveled from my country to western Europe in 1697 and toured shipyards, mines, and manufacturing facilities. I returned to my country determined to modernize it. I conquered a warm-water port on the Baltic and built a new city to be my "window on the west." When the men of my country refused to cut their beards and adopt a more modern look, I set up a "beard tax." I even took up the scissors myself and cut off a few beards.

Who am I and what nation did I rule?

82

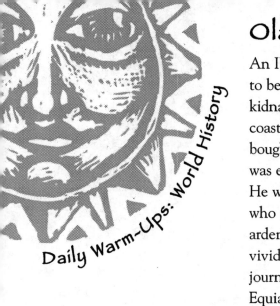

Olaudah Equiano (1745–1797)

An Ibo from the Kingdom of Benin, Olaudah Equiano was expected to be a tribal leader like his father. When he was 11, he was kidnapped and sold into slavery. Taken by British slavers on the coast, he went first to Barbados and then to Virginia. Equiano was bought by a British naval officer and taken to England, where he was educated. He accompanied his master on many ship voyages. He was ultimately sold to a Quaker merchant from Philadelphia who allowed him to buy his freedom in 1766. Equiano became an ardent **abolitionist.** In 1789 he wrote his autobiography. In it, he vividly described the "middle passage," the horrific transatlantic journey from Africa to America made by slaves. Ten years after Equiano's death in 1797, the British abolished the slave trade and worked to end it worldwide.

Why is Olaudah Equiano's story particularly remarkable?

83

Louis XIV

Louis XIV rarely talked at meals. He preferred to eat—in huge quantities. A typical supper for Louis was four bowls of soup, an entire chicken, a pheasant, two slices of ham, a salad, some mutton, pastry, fruit, and hard-boiled eggs. Louis's dinner was often a ritual. It could be eaten "au petit couvert" (with family and friends) or "au grand couvert" (a state banquet with many attendants). Occasionally, Louis would dine "au public." This meant tourists could go to Versailles to watch the king eat. The public would move in through one door and out another in a line while the king consumed his meal. Louis had many ways to keep the public enthralled with his role as the Sun King.

Daily Warm-Ups: World History

84

How did the building of his palace at Versailles reinforce the notion that Louis was the center of the French nation?

© 2002 J. Weston Walch, Publisher

The Black Hole of Calcutta, 1756

Throughout the eighteenth century, the British and the French were colonial and political rivals on a worldwide scale. These two powers fought wars in North America, the European mainland, and India. The French in India tried to influence local Indian princes to turn against the British. In 1756 an Indian official, the nawab of Bengal, captured the British stronghold of Calcutta. He locked 146 Europeans into a small dungeon. This room was about 18 feet by 18 feet, with very small barred windows. It was the height of the summer heat. By morning, 120 of the prisoners had suffocated. This became known as the "Black Hole of Calcutta" and caused great outcry among the British.

How did the British react? What was the result of this tragedy?

85

© 2002 J. Weston Walch, Publisher

Matteo Ricci

One of the first contacts with China in the age of European expansion was made by Christian **missionaries,** notably an Italian Jesuit named Matteo Ricci. A man of great intellectual gifts, Ricci learned Chinese and dressed as a Confucian scholar. He worked in China to convert the Chinese to Christianity from 1582 until his death in 1610.

Why is Matteo Ricci's mission typical of this era in the history of the Catholic Church? What was happening in Europe at this time that would cause missionaries to transverse the globe?

86

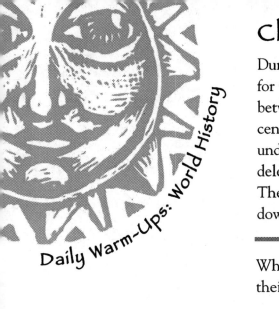

Chinoiserie

During the eighteenth century, Europeans developed a great desire for Chinese goods. This fad was known as *chinoiserie*. At first, trade between the West and China was fairly open. By the eighteenth century, Europeans were restricted to one port, Canton, and only under severe regulations. The British government sent a delegation to China in 1793 to ask that other ports be opened. The Manchu emperor accepted gifts from the British, but turned down the Europeans' demands.

What did the Chinese have that the Europeans wanted for their homes?

87

Galileo

In 1992, the Roman Catholic Church righted a wrong it had inflicted upon a scientist in 1633. Pope John Paul II admitted that the Church had been wrong to bring Galileo Galilei before the Roman Inquisition for his scientific teachings. Galileo was shown the traditional instruments of torture used by the Inquisition. Then he was given the chance to recant (renounce) his views as heresy. Galileo was placed under house arrest in Florence for the rest of his life and forbidden to teach.

Daily Warm-Ups: World History

What did Galileo teach that was heresy to the church at that time?

88

Philosopher Matchup

Match each philosopher on the left with his most famous work on the right.

1. Voltaire

2. Baron de Montesquieu

3. Denis Diderot

4. Jean-Jacques Rousseau

5. John Locke

(a) *Social Contract*

(b) *The Encyclopedia*

(c) *The Spirit of the Laws*

(d) *Candide*

(e) *Two Treatises on Government*

89

Laissez-faire

In 1776, a Scottish professor, Adam Smith, published *Wealth of Nations*. This book became the foundation for **"laissez-faire"** economics.

In two or three sentences, what is "laissez-faire"? How did it differ from **mercantilism?**

90

There's a Fungus Among Us!

During the summer of 1789, the French peasants were extremely afraid that the nobility were going to send armed forces against them. Peasants burned *chateaux* and manorial records. They tried to arm themselves against any impending danger. One theory is that the peasants were affected mentally by a fungus growing on their poorly-stored and meager supplies of rye. This particular mold or fungus causes paranoia and delusions.

What else might account for the anxiety of the peasants of France during the summer of 1789? What political events were happening in the nation's capital that greatly concerned them?

91

The Insatiable Madame Guillotine

In 1789, Dr. Joseph-Ignace Guillotin appeared before the newly-formed National Assembly of France. He boasted that he had invented a new device to execute people: "Gentlemen, with my machine, I'll take off your head in a flash, and you won't even feel the slightest pain." During the Reign of Terror, 1793–94, thousands of victims lost their heads to the insatiable "Madame Guillotine," as the device became known. The guillotine remained the official method of execution in France until 1977.

What was the purpose of the Reign of Terror, other than to spill the blood of thousands? Did it meet its objective?

92

Experimentation vs. Experience

Writer Susan Dunn characterized the difference between the French Revolution and the earlier American Revolution as "experimentation vs. experience."

What does this mean? How can it account for the very different outcomes of the two revolutions?

93

Who Am I?

My country became the second republic in the Western Hemisphere after I led a revolt against French rule. This revolt was also the only successful slave revolt in history. I was born a slave in 1744 and was taught to read and write by a Roman Catholic priest. Because of my education, I worked as a domestic servant. When a slave revolt broke out in 1791, I helped my masters to escape, then joined the rebels. I organized an army of 20,000 that by 1797 controlled most of my island home. I wrote a constitution for my people that gave equality and citizenship to all inhabitants. Although I was eventually captured and died in a French prison in 1803, others were able to build on my victory. My nation became independent in 1804 and took the name "Haiti."

94

Who am I?

Napoleon's Tunnel

Today, travelers can travel under the English Channel from France to England through the Chunnel or Channel Tunnel. In the early part of the nineteenth century, one of Napoleon Bonaparte's schemes to defeat England was to build a tunnel. French soldiers could travel through it, avoiding Britain's powerful army. This tunnel was never built.

How did Napoleon try to defeat Britain? Was he successful?

95

© 2002 J. Weston Walch, Publisher

Dissenters

Abraham Darby of Coalbrookdale in England made an astounding breakthrough. He found he could use a type of coal called **coke** to smelt iron. This brought the cost of iron down dramatically and began a new industry. Abraham Darby was a Quaker. The most active people in getting the **Industrial Revolution** off the ground in Great Britain were the **dissenters,** people who did not belong to the Anglican Church. Dissenters could be Quakers, Congregationalists, Baptists, or Presbyterians. As dissenters, certain restrictions were placed on them; for example, they could not attend Oxford or Cambridge.

96

How did the dissenters get an education? How did this prepare them for an active role in the Industrial Revolution?

The Industrial Revolution

"The manner in which the great multitude of the poor is treated by society today is revolting. They are drawn into large cities where they breathe a poorer atmosphere than in the country; they are relegated to districts which, by reason of the method of construction, are worse ventilated than any others; they are deprived of all means of cleanliness, of water itself, since pipes are laid only when paid for, and the rivers so polluted that they are useless for such purposes; they are obliged to throw all offal and garbage, all dirty water, often all disgusting drainage and excrement into the streets, being without other means of disposing of them; they are thus compelled to infect the region of their own dwellings."

So wrote Friedrich Engels in 1845 in *The Condition of the Working Class in England*. In 1848 Engels and his friend Karl Marx wrote another book called *The Communist Manifesto*. How did this book address the problems of the working class? What solutions did Marx and Engels explore for the conditions described above?

97

Congress of Vienna

The **Congress of Vienna** began to meet in September 1814. Its mission was to put western Europe back together after all the changes caused by the reign of Napoleon. The representatives of the great powers were Lord Talleyrand, minister for Louis XVIII of France; Lord Castlereagh, prime minister of England; Count Hardenburg, representing Prussia; Prince Metternich, representing Austria; and Czar Alexander I, representing Russia.

What do these names and titles tell us about the goals of the Congress of Vienna?

98

Queen Victoria

She was only 18 years old when she took the throne in 1837. The British people were not terribly enthusiastic about her ability to rule and be a role model for the nation. When she died in 1901, the British were referring to her reign as the **Victorian Age** and to themselves as Victorians. Even in the United States, we speak of Victorian-style houses and Victorian furnishings.

What attributes did Victoria bring to the throne that eventually endeared her to the British people? Why did her name become associated with an age?

99

The Railway Age

In 1829, English inventor George Stephenson ran a steam-powered locomotive called "the Rocket" at an astounding speed of 28 miles per hour. The first railway line from Liverpool to Manchester began in 1830. Railroad companies soon began to spring up in earnest. By the middle of the nineteenth century, there were about 20,000 miles of tracks in Great Britain.

List some of the ways that the railways affected Britain socially and economically during this period.

100

Darwin Debate

On a Saturday in June 1860, 700 people attended a debate. The speakers were Samuel Wilberforce, the bishop of Oxford, and Professor Thomas Huxley, a noted **paleontologist.** The subject was Darwin's theory of evolution. Wilberforce, known as "Soapy Sam," tried to demean Huxley. He asked him if he was descended from a monkey through his grandfather or grandmother. Huxley, who was to win the nickname "Darwin's Bulldog," said he wasn't ashamed to have an ape as an ancestor. However, he would be ashamed to be related to a man who used his gifts to obscure the truth by using ridicule. In the uproar that followed, a woman fainted.

Why is Darwin's theory so controversial?

101

Suez Canal

In 1869, the Suez Canal opened. This man-made waterway linked the Mediterranean and the Red seas. Built by the French, it took nearly ten years to complete. It was later acquired by the British.

Why was the opening of the Suez Canal so important to the growth of European imperialism?

102

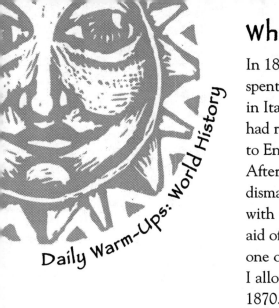

Who Am I?

In 1848, I was elected president of France although I hadn't really spent much of my life in that country. I was a military adventurer in Italy, had tried to overthrow the monarchy of Louis-Phillipe, and had received a life sentence to prison. In 1846, I escaped and went to England, but returned to France during the 1848 Revolution. After being elected president of the Second French Republic, I dismantled the republic in 1852 and proclaimed the Second Empire with myself as emperor. I helped to industrialize France. With the aid of Baron Haussman, I redesigned and beautified Paris, making it one of the grandest cities in the world. My weakness was diplomacy. I allowed myself to be drawn into a disastrous war with Prussia in 1870. While personally leading the army, I was captured by the Germans. My own people deposed me as emperor. I fled to England, where I died in 1873. My family name can account for a good deal of my mystique.

Who am I?

103

Italian Unification

Three men contributed to the unification of Italy in 1861. One has been called the "spirit of Italian unification." One is known as the "architect of Italian unification." The third is referred to as the "sword of Italian unification."

Who are they?

104

Who Said This?

"The great questions of the day will not be settled by speeches or majority votes—that was the great mistake of 1848 and 1849—but by blood and iron."

Who said this? What did he mean?

105

South American Revolutions

Match each Latin American revolutionary on the left with the country on the right over which he was influential.

1. Simón Bolívar
2. Miguel de Hidalgo
3. Emperor Pedro I
4. Bernardo O'Higgins
5. José de San Martín

(a) Mexico
(b) Chile
(c) Argentina
(d) Brazil
(e) Venezuela

Daily Warm-Ups: World History

106

Opium Wars

During the 1800s, China had much that Europeans wanted. However, little that Europe had to offer appealed to the Chinese. This upset the balance of trade. The British began to import opium into China in the hopes that the demand for this addictive drug would swing the balance of trade in the favor of the British. The Chinese government protested against the opium trade. Two wars were fought between Britain (later joined by France) and China. Both times the Europeans were successful.

List the results of these opium wars for China.

107

Meiji Era in Japan

The **Meiji Era** in Japan was a golden age in Japanese history. People were freed from the restrictions of the Tokugawa **shogunate** and could learn of the outside world. The spirit was one of creative energy.

How did the Meiji Era help Japan escape the fate of China in the late nineteenth century?

108

Artist Matchup

Match each artist on the left with the appropriate style or period of art on the right.

1. Jacques-Louis David
2. Joseph Mallord William Turner
3. Claude Monet
4. Vincent van Gogh
5. Pablo Picasso

(a) postimpressionism
(b) classicism
(c) cubism
(d) romanticism
(e) impressionism

109

Who Am I?

First came a degrading ceremony where I was stripped of my rank as a French army officer. This included watching my sword being broken in two. Then, on January 5, 1895, I was sent to the prison on Devil's Island. I was accused of treason on the flimsiest of evidence. Some people in France continued to support my cause. They believed that I was being persecuted for being a Jew. The novelist Emile Zola wrote an open letter to a newspaper. It started with the now famous words "J'accuse" (I accuse), and attacked the military and the courts for their dishonesty. I was finally exonerated in 1906. "L'affaire," as my case was called, changed the nature of French politics. It made the world aware of the intense anti-Semitism in Europe.

110

Who am I?

Suffrage Movements

By the end of the nineteenth century, there were many movements that sought to gain the right to vote for women. The strongest movement was in Great Britain. It included organizations like the Women's Social and Political Union led by Emmeline Pankhurst. Since the key thing that women wanted was **suffrage,** or the right to vote, these activists were called **suffragettes.** Some suffragettes resorted to violence to make their voice heard. They smashed shop windows, bombed railway stations, engaged in arson, or chained themselves to public monuments.

When did women in Great Britain receive the right to vote? Was the violence successful in achieving this aim?

111

Patterns of Immigration

Throughout history, there have been movements of people. However, the nineteenth and early twentieth centuries saw one of the most extensive mass migrations of people, particularly people traveling across the Atlantic from Europe to the Americas. Hundreds of thousands of English, Scots, Irish, Germans, Italians, and Russian Jews, to name just a few groups, left their homelands. They sought a better life in the Western Hemisphere. Many settled in the United States. Some of these immigrants made their money in America and returned to Europe. Most remained in their adopted country.

112

On a sheet of paper, draw two columns. Label one "Push" and the other "Pull." List in each column factors that might have pushed people out of their homeland or factors that might have pulled people to America.

Young Turks

In today's business world, the term "Young Turk" means someone who is a risk-taker and a bit of a rebel.

Who were the original "Young Turks" of the late nineteenth century?

The Scramble for Africa

In 1884–85, the chancellor of Germany, Otto von Bismarck, called a conference at Berlin. The conference was to discuss how European states should acquire colonies in Africa. Bismarck personally thought colonies were a waste of effort for a great power. Still, he recognized the growing tensions over unclaimed African territories and wanted to avoid a general European war over imperialistic aims. After the Berlin Conference, the mad scramble for Africa began.

By 1900, only two territories in Africa remained independent of European control. What were they?

114

Isandlwana

In January 1879, one of the most disastrous battles in the history of the British army occurred at Isandlwana in southern Africa. About 1,700 well-armed British soldiers died in a battle with spear-carrying Zulu warriors. The subject of several motion pictures, the Zulu Wars were a sordid chapter in the history of **imperialism.**

What drove the British and other European countries to claim large tracts of land in Africa and Asia?

Dr. Sun Yat-sen

Dr. Sun Yat-sen was a medical doctor. He was born a peasant but studied English in Hawaii and medicine in Canton and Hong Kong. He was one of the leaders of China's 1911 revolution against Manchu rule. Sun Yat-sen believed strongly in what he called the "Three Principles of the People"—nationalism, livelihood, and democracy or rights.

What did Sun mean by emphasizing these principles for China?

116

Russo-Japanese War

President Theodore Roosevelt won the Nobel Peace Prize for bringing Russia and Japan together for a treaty ending the **Russo-Japanese War** of 1904–05. The Japanese had destroyed Russia's Pacific and Atlantic fleets and had won victories on land as well.

Why was the outcome of this war so surprising to the western world?

117

Battleship *Potemkin*

Every student of film is familiar with Sergei Eisenstein's 1925 film *The Battleship Potemkin*. This early cinema classic is famous for its editing techniques. However, many people are less familiar with the historical background to the plot. This involves a mutiny on board a Russian battleship during the 1905 revolution. This revolution was called by Lenin a "dress rehearsal" for a later revolution.

What caused the 1905 revolution? Was it successful?

118

Scientist Matchup

The period from 1850–1914 has been characterized as the **Age of Progress.** Nowhere was this progress more evident than in science and invention. Match each scientist on the left with his or her most famous discovery on the right.

1. Sigmund Freud
2. Marie Curie
3. Alexander Graham Bell
4. Ivan Pavlov
5. Robert Koch
6. Max Planck
7. Albert Einstein

(a) quantum mechanics
(b) the telephone
(c) theory of relativity
(d) theory that bacteria cause disease
(e) discovery of radium
(f) psychiatry
(g) conditioned reflex theory

119

Titanic

More than the subject of an Academy Award-winning movie, the ship *Titanic* has become a symbol of an age gone by. It represented a time when western Europe and the United States felt there was nothing they could not accomplish technologically.

How has the sinking of the *Titanic* in April 1912 come to symbolize the increasing sense of uncertainty that led up to World War I?

Paris Exhibition of 1900

The last years of the nineteenth century would later be remembered by Europeans as "La Belle Epoque," the beautiful era, a time of promise and progress. In 1900, to welcome the new century, Paris hosted an international exhibition. It celebrated the new prosperity that was being experienced.

What new inventions that were heralded at the beginning of the twentieth century made some people optimistic about the future?

121

The Powder Keg of Europe

In the early years of the twentieth century, the area of the Balkans was known as the powder keg or tinderbox of Europe. This was due to the volatile politics in this area.

Divide a sheet of paper into two columns. In one column, list the countries of the Balkans as they were at the outbreak of World War I. In the other column, list the Balkan countries today.

122

Who Am I?

My father only reigned for 100 days before dying of throat cancer. I became kaiser, to the dismay of many. I was the grandson of Queen Victoria and she was the only person I felt I had to obey. I was an aggressive leader who loved the military. I thought that democracy demonstrated weakness. Born with a withered arm, I compensated for my disability by always appearing in a specially made military uniform and emphasizing strength and power. I dismissed my chancellor, Bismarck, because I wanted to run the country without his interference. I led my country into World War I, but was forced to abdicate at the end of the war. I died in exile in 1941.

Who am I?

123

Zimmerman Telegram

The Zimmerman telegram was a tremendous shock to the American public. It was printed in many newspapers in the United States in 1917. This telegram was sent by the German secretary for foreign affairs to the German minister in Mexico. It told him to inform the Mexican government that, if there was a war between Germany and the United States, Germany would ally itself with Mexico. Also, if a war broke out, Germany would support Mexico in reclaiming territories it had lost to the United States in the 1840s—Texas, New Mexico, and Arizona. (Zimmerman left out California for some reason!) American opinion was rapidly moving against Germany during this time.

124

What were some other reasons that the United States finally declared war on Germany in April 1917?

World War I

The English poet Siegfried Sassoon wrote "I am staring at a sunlit picture of Hell" while viewing the carnage of World War I.

What technological innovations in this war caused it to become a **war of attrition,** a war in which the objective was to deplete the enemy's human and material resources until they could no longer fight?

125

© 2002 J. Weston Walch, Publisher

Woodrow Wilson in Paris

Thomas Woodrow Wilson was a historian, former president of Princeton University, governor of New Jersey, and president of the United States. In 1919, as Europe lay in ruins, all eyes were on Wilson as he arrived in Paris for the peace talks. Wilson had announced his Fourteen Points for Peace in January 1918, while the war was still in full force. This document was even dropped behind the German lines. Georges Clemenceau, the premier of France, was heard to say "Wilson bores me with his Fourteen Points. Why, the good Lord himself has only ten."

What happened to the Fourteen Points at the Paris Peace Conference? Why was Clemenceau's viewpoint indicative of the intentions of the allied powers in 1919?

126

Siberian Exile Camp

From the end of the nineteenth century into the twentieth century, thousands of Russian **dissidents** were sent east of the Ural Mountains into Siberia. V. I. Lenin was exiled to Siberia in 1897. The purpose of exiling people who were a threat to the Russian government was to get them away from civilization and to isolate them. In reality, Siberia has been called the best "university" for revolutionaries.

Why might this be so?

Rasputin

Grigori Rasputin was a self-proclaimed holy man. He captivated the royal family of Russia by his supposed ability to control the bleeding of the heir to the throne, who had hemophilia. The Czarina Alexandra was not popular to begin with. Some people thought she was a German spy. Her reliance on Rasputin and his control of the royal family—and thus the Russian government—led many to declare the czar's actions treasonable. Two young aristocrats took it upon themselves to assassinate Rasputin. They fed him huge amounts of cyanide, shot him at close range, and finally, beat and bound him and shoved him under the ice of the Neva River. When the body was discovered, it was found that he had died by drowning!

128

Rasputin was one reason for the unrest that caused the Russian Revolution in March 1917. List some of the other reasons.

Who Am I?

I was born in 1879. My real name was Lev Davidovich Bronstein. I became an active revolutionary at the age of 19 and was jailed many times. I took the name that I am known by from one of my jailers. A brilliant orator, I became Lenin's right-hand man. I masterminded the Bolshevik overthrow of the Provisional Government in November 1917. I founded the Red Army and pushed it to victory in the Russian Civil War. After Lenin's death, I became a victim of Joseph Stalin. He was able to push me out of power and exile me from the Soviet Union in 1929. I was assassinated by Stalinist agents in Mexico in 1940.

Who am I?

129

© 2002 J. Weston Walch, Publisher

Who Were They?

In the early 1920s in Italy, a group of black-shirted ruffians beat up and force-fed castor oil to Communists, Socialists, and anyone else they thought was a threat to national order. This group was led by a World War I veteran named Benito Mussolini. Mussolini claimed that he was a patriotic nationalist who would lead Italy to greatness.

What did Mussolini's group call itself? How were they able to gain popular support in Italy?

130

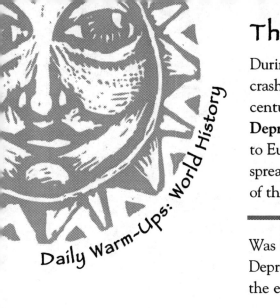

The Depression

During a week in October 1929, the American stock market crashed. This ushered in the worst depression in the twentieth century, a depression so serious that it is referred to as the "**Great Depression.**" The depression spread rapidly from the United States to Europe, not yet recovered from the First World War. Then it spread to the rest of the world, demonstrating the global nature of the economy.

Was it just the crash of the stock market that sparked the Great Depression? What underlying causes were there for the collapse of the economy?

131

Who Wrote This?

"If we were to divide mankind into three groups, the founders of culture, the bearers of culture, the destroyers of culture, only the Aryan could be considered as the representative of the first group. From him originate the foundations and walls of human creation, and only the outward form and color are determined by the changing traits of character of the various peoples. He provides the mightiest building stones and plans for all human progress . . . ."

Who wrote this?

132

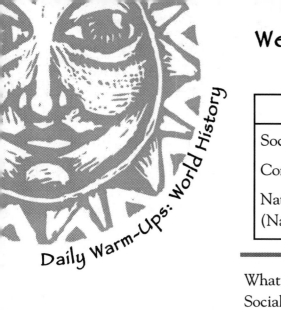

Weimar Republic Elections

Number of Deputies Elected to Reichstag

	1928	1930	1932	1933
Social Democrats	153	143	133	120
Communists	54	77	89	81
National Socialists (Nazis)	12	107	230	288

What does this graph tell you about the rise of the National Socialist Party in Weimar Germany? What can explain the rise to power of the Nazis between 1928 and 1933?

133

The Five-Year Plans

In 1928, Joseph Stalin began the first five-year plan to modernize and industrialize the Soviet Union.

Was this plan successful in achieving its aims?

134

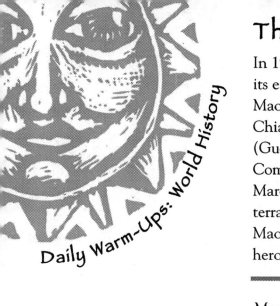

The Long March

In 1921, the Communist Party was organized in China. One of its earliest members was a former teacher and librarian named Mao Zedong. Mao's biggest rival for power was Jiang Jieshi or Chiang Kai-shek, the leader of the Nationalism Party in China (Guomindang). When the Nationalists moved to eliminate the Communists in 1934, Mao led his followers on the legendary "Long March." This march of over 6,000 miles through some of the worst terrain in China caused the death of thousands. However, it gained Mao much support among the Chinese people and made him a hero in the eyes of many.

Mao's theory of communism was different from orthodox Marxism. How did the Long March reflect Mao's approach to communism?

135

Gandhi and the Spinning Wheel

Great Britain placed many restrictions upon its colony of India. Among them was the law that Indians could not spin their own thread and weave their own cloth. Britain wanted the Indians to buy cloth from the mother country. Mohandas K. Gandhi taught **passive resistance** to British rule. One of his actions was to work a hand spinning wheel while he spoke to his followers—an action in defiance of the British authorities but nonviolent in its nature.

How are Gandhi and his spinning wheel remembered today as part of the symbol of the nation of India?

136

Kemal Atatürk

After World War I, the Allies agreed to divide up Turkey, which had fought on the losing side. They looked upon the former Ottoman Empire as hopelessly backward. An energetic army officer named Mustafa Kemal turned the tide. Taking the name "Atatürk" or "Father of the Turks," Kemal modernized Turkey and resisted the Allies. He became the first president of Turkey. His reforms included abolishing the office of caliph, discouraging women from wearing the veil, and substituting a Latin script for Arabic letters. Turkey became the first Islamic state to westernize, modernize, and maintain its independence.

What happened to the other Middle Eastern Islamic states after World War I?

137

© 2002 J. Weston Walch, Publisher

Italy and Ethiopia

In 1935, Mussolini led Italy into a war to conquer Ethiopia and turn it into an Italian colony. Mussolini was successful. He integrated Ethiopia with Somaliland into Italian East Africa.

Why did Mussolini invade Ethiopia? Why was this important for Italian national pride?

138

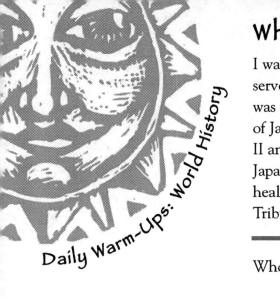

Who Am I?

I was a graduate of the Imperial Military Academy in Japan and served as a military attaché in Berlin after World War I. In 1940, I was appointed minister of war. A year later I became prime minister of Japan. I dominated the government of Japan during World War II and was very aggressive in leading my country's war effort. After Japan's surrender, I tried to kill myself, but I was nursed back to health to stand trial as a war criminal. The International Military Tribunal found me guilty and I was hanged.

Who am I?

139

Abraham Lincoln Brigade

The Spanish Civil War raged from 1936–39. It was one of many events that made the 1930s a time of incredible tension. Called a "dress rehearsal" for World War II, the civil war split world public opinion into pro- and anti-fascist camps. Although the United States and Britain pledged neutrality, young men from both countries enlisted as volunteers for the Loyalist forces. Many joined the "Abraham Lincoln Brigade" to fight in the war. The American novelist Ernest Hemingway was a volunteer.

What countries did actively intervene in the Spanish Civil War? What side did they support?

140

Novelist Matchup

Match each early twentieth-century novelist on the left with his or her most famous work on the right.

1. James Joyce
2. Virginia Woolf
3. Marcel Proust
4. John Galsworthy
5. Erich Maria Remarque

(a) *A Room of One's Own*
(b) *The Forsyte Saga*
(c) *Ulysses*
(d) *All Quiet on the Western Front*
(e) *Remembrance of Things Past*

© 2002 J. Weston Walch, Publisher

"Peace in Our Time"

The newly-formed British Broadcasting Corporation (BBC) captured for television the image of Prime Minister Neville Chamberlain as he returned to England from Munich. Chamberlain proclaimed that he had brought "peace with honor. I believe it is peace for our time."

How did the Munich Crisis demonstrate the weakness of the western European democracies?

142

The Nazi-Soviet Pact

On August 23, 1939, the Western European powers were shocked when Germany and the Soviet Union signed the Nazi-Soviet nonaggression pact.

Why was this pact so devastating and so unexpected to Britain and France? Why was this pact looked upon as the last prelude to World War II?

143

© 2002 J. Weston Walch, Publisher

Dunkirk Evacuation

In June 1940, as Hitler advanced to conquer France, the British Expeditionary Force was trapped on the beach at Dunkirk. Fortunately, Hitler stopped the advance of his armored divisions. In a rescue of epic proportions, the British succeeded in evacuating over 330,000 troops, including some French. To do this, the government called on the cooperation of anyone who had a boat that could cross the channel—pleasure craft, fishing boats, even the royal yacht. On one fishing boat, the soldiers lay down in rows in the hold like herrings to cram in as many as possible. The equipment was left behind, but most of the British army was saved in this effort of civilian cooperation.

144

How else did British civilians aid the war effort? What sacrifices did they make?

The Rape of Nanking

It is sometimes called the "Forgotten Holocaust" of World War II. In December 1937, the Japanese army invaded China. They took over the city of Nanking, embarking on a six-week rampage of terror. The Japanese army killed up to 500,000 civilians. The Japanese government has not acknowledged that it occurred.

What countries other than China did the Japanese conquer in their Pacific "blitzkrieg"?

145

The Infamous Railway Car

On June 22, 1940, Hitler realized his dream and signed an **armistice** with France. The armistice was signed in northern France at the same location where Germany had signed the armistice on November 11, 1918, that ended World War I. Hitler had the railway carriage where Germany had surrendered pulled into the French park commemorating World War I. He even had the same table and chairs, and he sat in the chair occupied by the French General Foch, who had concluded the German surrender. The railway carriage was then brought to Berlin and put on display until allied bombers destroyed it toward the end of the war.

146

Why was the symbolism of this railway carriage so important to Hitler? What did it say to the German people?

World War II Leaders' Words

Match each World War II leader on the left with the quotation attributed to him on the right.

1. Winston Churchill
2. Franklin Delano Roosevelt
3. Charles de Gaulle
4. Joseph Stalin
5. General Douglas MacArthur

(a) "I shall return!"

(b) "... this was their finest hour."

(c) "All working people must be roused to defend our freedom, our honor, our country . . . ."

(d) ". . . a day which will live in infamy."

(e) "France has lost a battle, but France has not lost the war."

147

An Important Part of the War Effort

At a rural estate in the English countryside of Buckinghamshire, one of the most important efforts of World War II was conducted by mathematicians. Bletchley Park today is a national historic site. Visitors can see where geniuses like Alan Turing worked to give Britain an edge against Nazi Germany.

What went on at Bletchley Park that was so significant to the British war effort?

148

The Wannsee Conference

On January 20, 1942, one of the most fateful meetings of Nazi officials took place at Wannsee, a suburb of Berlin. It was attended by the leaders of the SS and presided over by Reinhard Heydrich. This conference was a huge triumph for the SS and its head, Heinrich Himmler. Probably over 50,000 Germans participated in the horrific results of this conference, where the words "the final solution" were used for the first time.

What was the outcome of this conference?

149

© 2002 J. Weston Walch, Publisher

The Manhattan Project

Scientist Robert Oppenheimer said this about a project that he and many other scientists worked on during the years of the Second World War: "You go ahead and do it and you argue about what to do about it only after you have had your technical success. . . . I don't think anybody opposed making it; there were some debates about what to do with it after it was made."

What were Oppenheimer and others working on in the so-called Manhattan Project?

150

"Iron Curtain" Speech

In March 1946, less than a year after the end of World War II, Winston Churchill gave a speech at Fulton, Missouri. In it, he said these famous lines: "From Stettin in the Baltic to Trieste in the Adriatic, an iron curtain has descended across the Continent."

To what was Churchill referring?

151

The State of Israel

On May 14, 1948, David Ben-Gurion proclaimed the existence of the Jewish state of Israel. This was the result of a two-year war between Jewish Zionist groups, the Arabs, and the British. Israel was immediately invaded by the armies of Egypt, Jordan, Syria, Lebanon, and Iraq, who vowed to push the Jews into the sea. The Arabs were not successful and the state of Israel stood firm.

Why did the British pull out of Palestine in 1948? What other problems were they facing at the time?

152

The Candy Bombers

From June 1948 to May 1949, the Allies flew millions of tons of supplies into the city of West Berlin, a city they had bombed three years earlier. Gasoline, coal, and goods were delivered to keep the residents alive. Some pilots even became known as "candy bombers" because they dropped little parachutes containing candy to the children of West Berlin.

Why was the Berlin airlift necessary? What did it accomplish?

153

NATO

Fear of the encroachment of communism into Western Europe led to the formation of the **North Atlantic Treaty Organization** (NATO) in 1949. This organization joined the United States, Canada, and the Western allies into a defensive alliance. It provided for American troops to be stationed throughout Europe. West Germany joined NATO in 1955.

What was the Communist response to NATO?

154

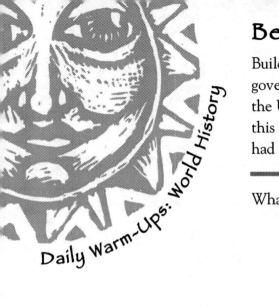

Beveridge Report and Welfare State

Building on a 1942 plan called the Beveridge Report, the Labour government embarked on a program to bring the welfare state to the United Kingdom. One of the earliest and most visible signs of this effort was free milk provided to schoolchildren, many of whom had suffered from poor nutrition during the war years.

What are some other characteristics of a welfare state?

155

Who Am I?

I was born to a very poor family in Argentina. However, being ambitious, I moved to Buenos Aires and became an actress. In 1945, I married an army colonel and supported him in his campaign for president of Argentina. I became his most powerful asset, particularly due to the support of the masses whom I called the "shirtless ones." I worked on behalf of the lower classes. They adored me, and even tried to have me canonized as a saint after my death. I died of cancer in 1952. A popular Broadway musical about me uses my nickname.

Who am I?

156

Korean War

The Korean War was ostensibly fought by United Nations forces. However, the United States provided most of the equipment and most of the troops.

How did this war illustrate the policy of **containment** after World War II?

157

The Cuban Revolution

Up until 1959, the "fun and sun" spot in the Caribbean was Havana, Cuba. Many Americans went there to gamble and enjoy nightclubs and resorts. That changed when Fidel Castro overthrew the corrupt military **dictatorship** of Fulgencio Batista. Castro took over American investments, restricted civil liberties, and accepted Soviet military aid. In 1961, Castro announced that Cuba was to become a Communist state. One result of this was the Cuban Missile Crisis of 1962. During this crisis, many thought that there was a very real possibility of a third world war.

What was this crisis, and how was it resolved?

158

What Nation Is This?

One of the most populated nations in the world, this country is made up of several thousand Pacific islands. The islands possess great mineral wealth, such as oil and gas. Formerly controlled by the Dutch, this nation has had a history of political instability. At the end of the twentieth century, it suffered a serious financial crisis caused by government mismanagement and corruption. The majority of the people are Muslim. This nation suffers from over-population, unemployment, and a low standard of living.

What nation is this?

159

Nuclear "Club"

One of the scariest results of postwar tensions was the proliferation of nuclear weapons. One by one, nations began to join what has been called "the nuclear club," meaning that they have the capability to use nuclear weapons.

Who are the members of "the nuclear club"?

160

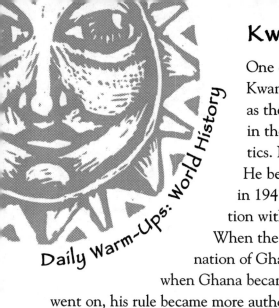

Kwame Nkrumah

One of the most controversial figures in postcolonial Africa was Kwame Nkrumah. Nkrumah was born in the British colony known as the Gold Coast. He was well educated, both in his homeland and in the United States. He was interested in pursuing a career in politics. Nkrumah believed in Pan-Africanism and favored socialism. He became an activist for African independence. He returned home in 1947, where he became involved in mass protests and noncooperation with colonial officials. As a result, he was jailed by the British. When the Gold Coast and Togoland became the independent African nation of Ghana in 1957, Nkrumah became the first prime minister. Later, when Ghana became a republic, he became its first president. As time went on, his rule became more authoritarian. His poorly thought-out development schemes put the country into debt and caused widespread labor unrest. In 1966, when Nkrumah was visiting Beijing, the army seized control and he was deposed. He died in exile in 1972. Nkrumah was typical of African leaders of this period in that he meant the best for his nation, but his government fell into corruption and incompetence.

161

What problems faced the new African nations?

The Mau Mau

For Europeans who had settled in Africa while it was under colonial rule, the movements for independence were disquieting and often violent. One of the most terrifying was a movement called the Mau Mau Society.

What was this society and how did the colonial authorities react to it?

Hungarian Freedom Fighter

Every year, *Time* magazine selects a Person of the Year. The selection process is based on how often the person has appeared in the news during the past year, not on whether that person has made a positive or negative impact. (Hitler was Man of the Year!) The Man of the Year for 1956 was the Hungarian Freedom Fighter.

What was a Hungarian Freedom Fighter? What happened in Hungary in 1956 that resulted in over 200,000 Hungarians fleeing their country and thousands being killed or sent to Siberia?

163

We Will Bury You!

The Scene: The United Nations General Assembly. A heavy-set man in an ill-fitting suit takes his shoe off and bangs it on the desk in front of him, shouting "We will bury you!"

Who is this man and why is he behaving in such a manner?

164

China's Cultural Revolution

In 1966, Mao Zedong launched the Great Proletarian Cultural Revolution. This was to combat what he considered to be weakness and revisionism in communism and in Chinese life in general.

How did the Cultural Revolution actually set back Chinese economic development and nearly destroy China's educational system?

165

Who Am I?

I founded the Indochina Communist Party and its successor, the Viet Minh, and was president of North Vietnam. I was born in French Indochina in 1890 to a poor family. I later moved to France where I worked as a gardener, a waiter, and a photo retoucher, among other jobs. In 1919, I petitioned the Versailles Peace Conference for more independent rule in Indochina. I was ignored, but became a hero to my people. I fought the Japanese during World War II. After they were defeated in 1945, I turned against the French colonial power and formed the Viet Minh, a group dedicated to independence. My country was split into a Communist and a noncommunist nation after independence. War between the two nations later involved the United States. Still, I am regarded as one of the most instrumental advocates of national communism in the twentieth century.

Who am I?

166

Watson and Crick

In 1953, an Englishman named Francis Crick and an American named James Watson discovered the molecular structure of DNA. This is the material in a cell's chromosomes that carries genetic information.

How did the discovery of the double helix cause people to consider both the promises and pitfalls that this knowledge might provide?

Made in Japan

Japan's recovery after World War II was rapid. Ten years after the war, Japan's standard of living was the highest in Asia. During the 1960s, Japanese companies took advantage of its well-educated workforce and produced electronics products of the highest quality. Japan dominated the electronics market during the last part of the twentieth century and on into the twenty-first.

Can you think of Japanese corporations that produce electronics products that you see in stores or might own yourself? List as many as you can.

168

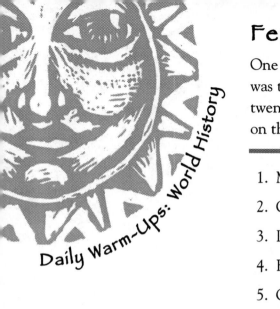

Female World Leaders

One result of the women's movement of the twentieth century was the emergence of women as leaders of nations. Match each twentieth-century leader on the left with the country she governed on the right.

1. Margaret Thatcher
2. Golda Meir
3. Indira Gandhi
4. Benazir Bhutto
5. Corazon Aquino

(a) the Philippines
(b) India
(c) the United Kingdom
(d) Israel
(e) Pakistan

169

Who Said This?

"America is the number-one enemy of the deprived and oppressed people of the world. . . . Let the Muslim nations be aware that Iran is a country effectively at war with America, and that our martyrs—the brave young men of our army and the Revolutionary Guards—are defending Iran and the Islam we hold dear against America. . . . We are ready to be killed and we have made a covenant with God to follow the path of our leader, the Lord of the Martyrs."

Who said this?

170

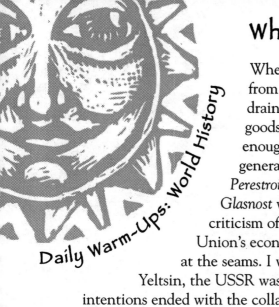

Who Am I?

When I came to power in 1985, the Soviet Union was suffering from an antiquated economy. A devastating war in Afghanistan was draining our resources. I recognized that our production of consumer goods was inadequate, our collective and state farms failed to produce enough food for our people, health care had deteriorated, and general demoralization had set in. I tried different methods of reform. *Perestroika* was the restructuring of the economy to decentralize it. *Glasnost* was the opening of Soviet society to more freedom and an open criticism of past policies. None of my efforts worked. Instead, the Soviet Union's economy disintegrated. Our multiethnic state began to come apart at the seams. I was pushed out of power in 1991. Under my successor, Boris Yeltsin, the USSR was dismantled into separate republics. All of my good intentions ended with the collapse of what had been one of the world's most powerful nations.

Who am I?

171

Polish Nationalism

In the Soviet satellites, the first country to see the end of communism was Poland. In 1990 Lech Walesa, the leader of the labor union Solidarity, was elected president of Poland in a free election. Poland was probably the most nationalistic of the eastern European countries. This national pride was furthered when Karol Cardinal Wojtyla was elected to a post of international importance in 1978.

What was this position?

172

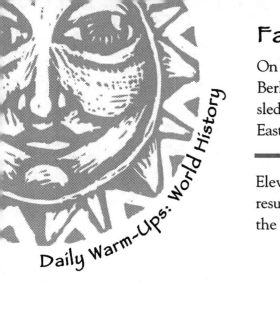

Fall of the Berlin Wall

On November 9, 1989, the world watched on television as Berliners climbed atop the Berlin Wall and attacked it with sledgehammers. Its destruction ended the separation between East and West Berlin that had existed since 1961.

Eleven months later, in October 1990, another event occurred as a result of the fall of communism and the symbolic dismantling of the Berlin Wall. What was it?

173

Tiananmen Square

In 1989, Chinese students demonstrated in Tiananmen Square in Bejing to show their support of democracy for China. The world watched for weeks as the students' numbers swelled. Finally, Deng Xiaoping ordered government troops out. Tanks rolled into the square and fired upon the unarmed protesters.

What were the results of the Tiananmen Square protest, both short-term and long-term?

Daily Warm-Ups: World History

174

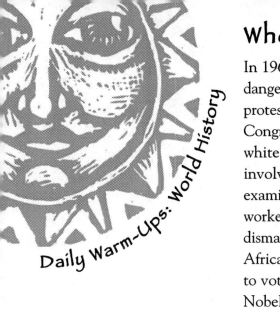

Who Am I?

In 1963, I was imprisoned by the South African government as a dangerous agitator. I was in jail for more than 27 years because I protested their policy of **apartheid.** I revived the African National Congress as a way to sponsor resistance to apartheid and the all-white rule of South Africa. A combination of black African involvement and an international boycott forced South Africa to examine its policies. In 1990, I was released from prison. I then worked with the president of South Africa, F. W. de Klerk, to dismantle apartheid and end the minority white rule. In 1994, South Africa held the first election in which black Africans were eligible to vote. I was elected president. In 1993, de Klerk and I received the Nobel Peace Prize for our efforts to bring about a peaceful settlement of South Africa's racial problems.

Who am I?

175

What Is This Place?

This city has a long and checkered history. In 1914, the heir
to the Austrian throne was assassinated here. The assassination
precipitated World War I. In 1984, the city was showcased to the
world as it hosted the winter Olympic games. It appeared to be
a model city, where people of different religious and ethnic
backgrounds could live together in peace. This changed in 1992.
Bosnian Serb forces bombarded the city and began a policy of
"ethnic cleansing." This eventually caused the United Nations
to establish the first international war crimes tribunal since the
Nuremberg Trials of 1945–46.

What is this city?

176

Common Market

This organization had its roots in the postwar **Marshall Plan.**
European states had to cooperate to receive funds. By 1956,
European economic cooperation had proved successful. It was so
successful that a number of European states came together in the
Treaty of Rome to form the **European Economic Community** or
Common Market.

What is this organization called today? How has it evolved over
the years to be more than just a common market of economic
trading partners?

177

© 2002 J. Weston Walch, Publisher

OPEC, GATT, IMF, WTO

Sometimes, while reading the newspaper, you can be faced with a bewildering array of initials designating different organizations, treaties, and the like.

What do these initials stand for?

OPEC   GATT   IMF   WTO

178

Popular Culture at the End of the Twentieth Century

One important aspect of popular culture at the end of the twentieth century was moving-image media—films and television. People rose to popularity and fell with astonishing rapidity. Can you match each media personality on the left with his most famous quote on the right?

1. John Cleese of Monty Python
2. Arnold Schwarzenegger in *The Terminator*
3. Clint Eastwood in *Dirty Harry*
4. Sir Alec Guiness as Obi Wan Kenobe
5. William Shatner in *Star Trek*

(a) "And now for something completely different!"
(b) "May the force be with you."
(c) "Beam me up, Scotty."
(d) "Go ahead, make my day!"
(e) "I'll be back!"

179

The Challenge of International Terrorism

On September 11, 2001, coordinated terrorist attacks destroyed the twin towers of the World Trade Center in New York City and a section of the Pentagon. One of the biggest challenges of the late twentieth and early twenty-first centuries has been how to deal with international terrorism.

Take one of the following terrorist groups and list its purpose and demands.

al Qaeda
IRA
Hamas
Red Brigade
Black September

180

1. Zinjanthropus was dated at 1.75 million years old—far older than any hominid found previously. It convinced the scientific community that human life forms had been on earth longer than previously imagined.
2. The man was obviously cared for by members of his community; this demonstrates the human emotion of compassion.
3. Neanderthals learned how to make fire. This enabled them to control one part of their environment.
4. When animals were harnessed to plows, men became the farmers and women tended the house.
5. Common remains that archaeologists find are things people throw away.
6. Important features would include a good area to fortify, such as a hilltop; location near trade routes; good water supply; and farmland for growing crops. Jericho had these features.
7. There are clear parallels with the story of Noah and the ark. Historians believe there was a good deal of movement of peoples and communication between ancient cultures.
8. Scientists can learn about the diseases and nutrition of ancient people.
9. The tomb of King Tut. The great riches are indicative of the great wealth of Egypt.
10. Mohenjo-daro and Harappa
11. Agriculture, use of metals, governmental system, religious beliefs
12. Many of the world's religions and philosophies came into being during this time of warfare.
13. 1(b); 2(d); 3(e); 4(a); 5(c); Agatha Christie
14. Punishments were harsh and often involved retribution; parents had total control over their children, disobedience was strictly punished.
15. The Pharaoh Akhenaton or Amenhotep IV

Daily Warm-Ups: World History

16. The Great Wall of China
17. The Minoans were great sea traders and connected Egypt to the Aegean world. Their religious beliefs influenced the early Greeks. Zeus was believed to have been born in a cave in Crete. The Minoans may have been the model for early Greek political, social, and economic systems.
18. Ethical dualism—the belief that humans are free to choose between good and evil and receive reward or punishment in the afterlife depending upon their choice. Many scholars believe that Christians get the concepts of heaven and hell and the devil from Zoroastrianism.
19. Confucius
20. 1(b); 2(d); 3(e); 4(a); 5(c)
21. Hinduism—belief in a supreme universal soul that has three forms: Brahma, the creator; Vishnu, the preserver; and Shiva, the destroyer. Righteous living involves prayer, observing the caste system, and practicing nonviolence and charity. There is also a belief in incarnation. Animals may contain human souls so they should not be killed. The cow is considered sacred.

Buddhism—Buddha was opposed to the caste system. He taught that a person's life is full of suffering caused by desire. Suffering can be eliminated by following the eightfold path of righteous living, which includes controlling one's emotions and renouncing material gratification. By living a righteous life, a person can avoid reincarnation and enter a spiritual state of peace known as Nirvana.
22. The people of Judah were not assimilated into Babylonian culture. They maintained their religious belief in their God, Yahweh. The date of the Babylonian captivity is often considered the beginning of Judaism.

23. He standardized weights and measures, laws, and currencies; built roads and bridges; expanded the Great Wall; standardized Chinese writing script; and centralized local government.

24. *Metropolis*, *politics*, and *cosmopolitan* come from *polis*. *Agoraphobia*, which comes from *agora*, is fear of crowds or open spaces.

25. Pro—He tried to spread knowledge and learning, emphasized multiculturalism, founded cities on the Greek model to act as centers of learning, commerce, and culture.
    Con—He was a ruthless military man who executed his own soldiers; an egomaniac who would stop at nothing to conquer more territory.

26. January—Janus, the two-headed god, looking at both years; March—Mars, the Roman god of war; May—the goddess Maia; June—the goddess Juno; July—Julius; August—augustus (means revered one, title taken by Caesar); September—seventh month in the original Roman calendar; October—eighth month; November—ninth month; December—tenth month

27. Most Roman cities were laid out on a grid plan and had a central market, a forum, and a stadium or coliseum. Buildings incorporated the arch, the vault, and the dome; concrete was often used as a building material. The infrastructure of Roman cities included an excellent road system, including bridges and tunnels; a system of aquaducts brought fresh water to the city.

28. Goods—silk cloth, grain, porcelain, herbal medicines, gold, ivory, spices, precious gems, pearls, carpets, cotton cloth, dye goods, horses, Bactrian camels, dromedaries, metalwork, and glassware; Intangibles—religious ideas, political concepts, art and architectural

styles, poems, stories and myths, languages, music, clothing styles, mathematics and science, technology, military tactics, and diseases

29. He opened Christianity to gentiles, making it separate from Judaism; introduced emphasis on Jesus as a savior and the doctrine of original sin; began new churches throughout the eastern Mediterranean; his letters to early churches became part of the Christian gospel.

30. The ease with which corn could be grown enabled the Meso-American cultures to devote their time to building projects, science, artwork, and writing.

31. Most historians feel that it was the weakness of the Roman Empire that caused the fall of Rome. Rome had many problems: soil exhaustion, drought, epidemics, population decrease, increase of number of slaves, political corruption, and religious fragmentation brought about by the growth of Christianity.

32. Justinian's Code; building projects; a briefly successful attempt to reconquer the western part of the Roman Empire

33. The Bible is a compilation and is chronological. The Koran is divided into surahs (chapters) in no particular order. The Koran is considered the actual word of God (Allah); the Bible is recognized to be from many sources. The Koran is considered to be the absolute course for everything; the Bible does not have this broad authority.

34. You are in Mecca.

35. While Baghdad was a sophisticated city of culture and commerce, conditions in western Europe were quite primitive in comparison.

36. Polynesian peoples had a common origin despite the vast distances between the Polynesian islands.

37. Despite the fact that the Maya did not know the use of metals or have the wheel, they are

considered a civilization. They had a writing and mathematical system, a calendar, agriculture, complex religious, political, and social systems, and art and architecture.

38. 1(c); 2(a); 3(b); 4(e); 5(d)

39. the kingdom of Ghana

40. Petrine Theory; The eastern Christian Church did not accept the authority of the pope and developed differently.

41. Monks copied religious manuscripts; monasteries served as hospitals, took in travelers, experimented in farming techniques, and were centers of education.

42. P—unified much of western Europe, was crowned emperor by the pope; R—worked for an educated clergy, encouraged monasteries; I—founded new schools and encouraged a new style of handwriting; M—established an army; E—reformed the currency, encouraged trade; S—set up the feudal system

43. There was a population increase in Scandinavia that caused the people to look for new lands. They were seeking farmland in a more temperate climate, as well as loot. They settled in England, the Shetland and Orkney Isles, Ireland, the northern coast of France, Iceland, Greenland, Russia—a few even settled in Sicily.

44. Centralized empire, development of bureaucracy, maintenance of a stable peasant class, strict regulations on trade and commerce, development of central legal code

45. Chinese writing, Buddhism, Chinese administrative reforms to centralize government, new Japanese capital city of Nara modeled after Chinese capital Chang'an

46. 1066 was the date of the Battle of Hastings, which completed the Norman conquest of England.

47. Medieval histories tend to chronicle the lives

of men and ignore women. Women were only important as sources of dowries in marriage and often became political pawns in the game of medieval politics.

48. King John of England

49. 1(e); 2(f); 3(d); 4(b); 5(c); 6(g); 7(a)

50. The medieval student is writing home for money and complaining about how expensive the university is—not very different from what we find today. Medieval universities were only open to students who were studying for some level of the priesthood, the curriculum was limited to the seven liberal arts, and no females were permitted to attend. In some universities, the students hired and fired their professors. There were no organized sports teams!

51. Islam was strengthened; the Byzantine Empire was weakened. Feudalism was weakened due to the deaths of knights on crusades. Kings took advantage of crusades to tax people and extend their power. The Church was criticized for the crusades. Trade was opened with Muslims as they became the middlemen for all kinds of eastern goods.

52. Breakdown of trade, labor shortage, declining demand for goods caused prices to fall

53. Germany, Austria, the Czech Republic, parts of Italy, Belgium, the Netherlands, Switzerland, and eastern France

54. Henry wanted to reach India by sailing around the tip of Africa. Bartholmeu Dias first rounded the Cape of Good Hope in 1488, but the crew mutinied before he could reach India. Vasco da Gama reached India in 1498. Christopher Columbus encouraged Spain to try to reach the Indies by sailing west across the Atlantic.

55. Spain lost many educated people as they fled to other areas of Europe, Africa, or the New

World. Protestant ideas did not develop in Spain due to fear of the Inquisition.

56. It cut off trade between western Europe and the East; Turks were hostile to Christianity; Turks posed a military threat to western Europe and tried to expand west.
57. Marco Polo
58. Chinese Admiral Zheng He
59. Persia, China, and central Asia. They tried to conquer Japan but were driven away.
60. In the West, the king was at the top of the feudal hierarchy. In Japan, a military man known as the shogun was the real power—the emperor was a figurehead. European knights do not practice *seppuku*.
61. Because of stories like these, explorers expected to find cannibals and fantastic creatures when they came to new lands.
62. The kingdom of Mali
63. We now know that Africans were capable of

sophistication in building and organization.
64. They did not have writing or the wheel. They used a numerical aid called a *quipu* to record information. They used runners to deliver messages.
65. It was in the Aztec empire. The Spanish conquerors used human sacrifice to justify their overthrow of the Aztec empire.
66. They imported slaves from Africa so that they paid no wages for labor.
67. 1(c); 2(e); 3(a); 4(b); 5(d)
68. Humanist scholars approached classical and medieval manuscripts in a fresh new light and did not depend on the traditional commentaries. They engaged in textual criticism where they analyzed the language and attempted to correct any mistakes made in earlier translations.
69. Desiderius Erasmus
70. Spaniards unknowingly brought diseases to

which the Indians had no immunity.

71. chocolate, corn (maize), peppers, squash, tomatoes, vanilla
72. Indulgences—pardons for sins
73. 1(b); 2(c); 3(a); 4(d); 5(d)
74. Henry VIII's six wives
75. King Henry III and Henry Guise, the leader of the Catholic Party, were assassinated, and Henry of Navarre became King Henry IV in 1589. Henry IV converted to Catholicism and issued the Edict of Nantes to protect the Huguenots. Under Henry IV, France settled down to some years of internal peace and prosperity.
76. A combination of bad timing, the resourcefulness of the English naval commanders, and a great storm (which the English called "the Protestant wind") destroyed the armada. The war between Spain and the united provinces went on a number of years more, but Spain

was no longer one of the most powerful states.
77. Spain established a colony in St. Augustine, Florida, in 1565.
78. The background causes were both political and religious. Protestants wished to gain more territory and add Calvinism as an acceptable religion for the states of the Holy Roman Empire. The emperor wished to control his states and enforce Catholicism. The king of France supported the Protestant princes as they rebelled against the emperor, and everyone else in Europe hoped for spoils. The result was the total devastation of the German-speaking parts of the Holy Roman Empire and further fragmentation of the empire.
79. The Dutch
80. The Royalists had more gentlemen soldiers who were trained to fight in the tradition of knights. The turning point came when Oliver Cromwell and Thomas Fairfax formed the

New Model Army, a highly disciplined, highly trained, hand-picked group of soldiers for the Parliamentary force.

81. It was virtually bloodless with little or no fighting. It established that the king of England must rule under the law of the land and with the consent of Parliament. William and Mary had to agree to the Bill of Rights before they were granted the throne.

82. Peter the Great of Russia

83. Very few slaves ever received an education and even fewer were able to gain their freedom during this period.

84. Versailles was huge and extravagant and housed clergy, nobility, and the offices of government. Every event of the king's day, from rising in the morning to going to bed at night, was an elaborate ritual that involved the nobility and kept them occupied.

85. French forces and influence were driven out.

The English placed India under the control of the British East India Company.

86. During the Catholic Reformation there was a strong missionary spirit in the Roman Catholic Church. Catholics tried to gain converts outside Europe by sending missionaries to the New World and Asia.

87. The Chinese had silk cloth, porcelain, carved furnishings, spices, medicinal herbs, and tea.

88. Galileo was teaching that the sun, not the earth, was the center of the universe.

89. 1(d); 2(c); 3(b); 4(a); 5(e)

90. Laissez-faire is the economic theory that government should allow natural laws to operate in economics. It favors free trade with no tariffs and duties. Mercantilism held that countries should try to be totally self-sufficient; the government should control the economy and use restrictive tariffs to keep out goods from other nations.

91. The Third Estate of the Estates General had split from that body and had declared itself the National Assembly. After the fall of the Bastille, King Louis had forced the nobles and clergy to join the National Assembly.

92. The Reign of Terror was to stamp out resistance to the revolution and put down counter-revolution. Instead, it left bitter memories of republicanism for many French.

93. The Americans had a long history of self-government through representative forms of government. The French had no such experience.

94. François-Dominique Toussaint, better known as Toussaint-Louverture

95. Napoleon enacted the "Continental System," an economic boycott of Great Britain, and forced all of his allied and defeated countries to participate. It was not successful.

96. The dissenters set up their own schools, which offered a much more practical form of education than Oxford or Cambridge. The older universities were designed to prepare people for the Anglican clergy. Dissenters received training in practical subjects like accounting, math, and science.

97. Marx and Engels believed that the working class (**proletariat**) would overthrow their masters, the **bourgeoisie.** With the working class controlling the means of production, everyone would be equal. People would work according to their means and be paid according to their needs. With no class divisions, the workers would not suffer and society would be perfect.

98. They were aristocrats of the old regime and sought to restore the "liberties of Europe," the legitimate governments before Napoleon. They also wished to protect Europe from France.

99. Victoria was hardworking and morally upright. She had a large family, which demonstrated proper middle-class values. During her reign Britain was the most powerful nation on earth due to the Industrial Revolution, control of the seas, and colonial possessions.

100. The railway meant that heavy goods could be carried quickly and cheaply. It created a demand for products like coal and iron that were used to make railways and other industries, created new jobs, changed towns and neighborhoods as railways cut through areas. Since people could now travel, it began the resort industry and the growth of suburbs.

101. Christian fundamentalists accepted literally the Bible story that God created the world and humans in six days. Darwin's theory was startling to a world just coming to grips with new theories that life on earth was measured in millions of years.

102. It cut the time of the trip between Europe and Asia in half and allowed quicker passage of people and goods.

103. Louis Napoleon Bonaparte

104. Giuseppe or Joseph Mazzini is known as the "spirit of Italian unification"; Camillo di Cavour, the prime minister of Sardinia-Piedmont, is called the "architect of Italian unification"; Giuseppe Garibaldi is known as the "sword of Italian unification."

105. Otto von Bismarck, chancellor of Prussia. He meant that armed force would be more powerful than votes and assemblies in effecting German unification.

106. 1(e); 2(a); 3(d); 4(b); 5(c)

107. The Europeans received trading concessions from China and more ports were opened to them. China was weakened and unable to resist outside influences.

Daily Warm-Ups: World History

108. Japan was able to modernize and westernize. It built a strong army, navy, educational system, banking system, and modern economy. Unlike China, Japan was not taken over, but became an imperialist power in its own right.

109. 1(b); 2(d); 3(e); 4(a); 5(c)

110. Captain Alfred Dreyfus

111. Women over the age of 30 received the right to vote in Britain in 1918. The violence in the suffragette movement did not turn the tide. Women's roles in the war effort and their patriotism did.

112. Push—religious and political persecution, war and violence, lack of land, economic problems, famine, ethnic disputes, no educational opportunities, social stratification
Pull—cheap land, employment opportunities, religious tolerance, public education, political stability, social mobility

113. The Young Turks belonged to the organization the Ottoman Society for Union and Progress. Their aims were universal suffrage, human rights, freedom of religion, free public education, and secularization of the state.

114. Liberia, which was a protectorate of the United States, and Ethiopia, which the Italians tried unsuccessfully to conquer

115. The motives for imperialism were many and varied: fertile ground for missionary work, new lands for scientists to explore, raw materials for European industry, cheap labor, national power and prestige, humanitarian reasons, markets for manufactured goods, and to claim territory.

116. Nationalism—Chinese people need to think of themselves as a nation rather than part of a clan or village. Livelihood—China needs to rid itself of imperialist constraints; there must be modernization and reform of the land sys-

tem. Democracy—sovereignty of the people, but government should be by experts.

117. It was the first time an Asian country defeated a European power. It showed the strength of Japan and the weakness of Russia.

118. The revolution was caused by unrest due to loss of the Russo-Japanese War, labor unrest, the attack on unarmed marchers by the czar's troops on "Bloody Sunday," peasant discontent over lack of land, desire for a *duma* or representative assembly as well as a constitution. The revolution was not successful.

119. 1(f); 2(e); 3(b); 4(g); 5(d); 6(a); 7(c)

120. The *Titanic* represented the best in technology and in providing comfort and luxury. Its sinking made people realize that nothing was finite and perfect. It added to the growing cynicism that exploded during World War I.

121. Electricity, electric lighting, electric trams, telephone, automobile, chemical industry, steel industry, many electric appliances such as the refrigerator, fan, vacuum cleaner, sewing machine

122. Balkan countries in 1914: Croatia-Slavonia (part of Austria-Hungary), Bosnia and Herzegovina (part of Austria-Hungary), Serbia, Romania, Bulgaria, Albania, Greece, Montenegro, small part of the Ottoman Empire; Balkan countries today: Yugoslavia (Serbia), Bosnia-Herzegovina, Albania, Macedonia, Greece, Slovenia, Bulgaria, Romania, Croatia, part of Turkey

123. Kaiser Wilhelm II of Germany

124. German declaration of unrestricted submarine warfare; American munitions manufacturers pushed for entry into the war.

125. Poisonous gas, the machine gun, long-range artillery, the tank, the airplane, aerial bombing

126. The allies were vindictive toward Germany. They did not wish to honor any of the Fourteen Points that were not to their advantage.

127. In Siberia, many revolutionaries were out of contact with the rest of Russia, but they were in contact with one another.

128. Incompetence of the Russian government, the fact that Russia was losing the war, labor unrest, peasant unrest, desire for a more democratic form of government with civil rights

129. Leon Trotsky

130. Fascists. They played upon middle-class fears of a Communist takeover. They were supported by businessmen, patriots, and the middle class.

131. Too much buying on credit in all areas of the economy; wages had not kept up with prices; mass purchasing power couldn't keep up with the output of goods; worldwide agricultural depression throughout the 1920s; Americans had ceased buying European goods; American companies called in loans to European nations and industries

132. Adolf Hitler in *Mein Kampf*

133. The Great Depression was the key to the rise to power of the Nazi Party. Before 1929, their numbers were small. As the effects of the depression were felt, their numbers increased.

134. The industrial part of the plan was a success and factories were booming. Collectivization of agriculture caused famine and hardship as peasants destroyed their crops and livestock rather than give them up to the government.

135. Mao felt that the peasant, not the urban proletariat, was the true revolutionary. He gained power among the peasant class.

136. The Indian national flag has a representation of Gandhi's spinning wheel in its center.

137. Other Middle Eastern countries were divided up between the victorious powers and thus became mandates of either France or Great Britain. Turkey remained independent.

138. Ethiopia was the only independent African nation not under a colonial power. Italy had tried to conquer Ethiopia in the nineteenth century, but had been defeated.

139. Hideki Tojo

140. The Soviet Union supported the Loyalist forces with military advisers. Germany and Italy sent troops and materiel to the Spanish **falangists** or **fascists** under General Franco.

141. 1(c); 2(a); 3(e); 4(b); 5(d)

142. Chamberlain had appeased Hitler at the Munich Conference by allowing him to take the Sudetenland of Czechoslovakia.

143. Hitler had risen to power as an avowed anti-Communist, and the two nations were ideologically at opposite ends of the scale. Britain in particular had hoped that Germany and the Soviet Union might go to war with each other. Although the treaty had some secret provisions, it was clear that the Russians and Germans were going to split Poland between them. Britain and France had pledged themselves to uphold the integrity of Poland, so when Germany invaded Poland on September 1, 1939, they declared war on Germany two days later.

144. The British rationed food, petrol, clothing, and other essentials; they held drives to collect cans and pots and pans to melt into munitions; they joined the Home Guard, the Air Raid Patrol, and other organizations; factories worked around the clock; unions pledged not to strike; many children were evacuated from cities and sent to the country or even overseas for the duration of the war.

145. Korea, Indochina, Thailand, Burma, Indonesia, the Philippines, Formosa, many of the small Pacific Islands, parts of New Guinea

146. Hitler wanted to avenge the treatment of Germany after World War I. The German people believe that they had been tricked into signing the armistice and that Germany had not truly been defeated in World War I.

147. 1(b); 2(d); 3(e); 4(c); 5(a)

148. The world's first programmable computer was initiated at Bletchley Park. British scientists and mathematicians deciphered the code of the Enigma machine. This enabled them to learn German military secrets.

149. This conference is where the term "final solution" was applied to mean the wholesale extermination of European Jews.

150. The Manhattan Project developed the atomic bomb. It ushered in the nuclear age.

151. Churchill was referring to the Soviet Union's increasing control over eastern Europe and suppression of liberty there.

152. The British were facing problems in India and Greece, and had many domestic problems at home, including food shortages and the return to a peacetime economy. Britain had also supported the formation of a Jewish state, and felt compelled to honor that declaration.

153. The Soviets had closed off access to West Berlin, which could only be reached on land through the Soviet sector of Germany. By the airlift, the Allies demonstrated that they would not give up West Berlin to the control of the USSR.

154. Formation of the Warsaw Pact comprised of the USSR, East Germany, Poland, Czechoslovakia, Hungary, Bulgaria, Romania, and Albania.

155. Sometimes referred to as "cradle-to-grave" services, the welfare state usually had such

programs as national health insurance, sick leave benefits, unemployment compensation, maternity leave benefits, death benefits (insurance), and subsidies for university education. Many European states became welfare states in the years following World War II.

156. Eva Peron or "Evita"

157. The Korean War demonstrated that the United States was not going to allow the spread of communism, but would try to contain it to the regions where it existed in the years following World War II.

158. American spy planes discovered Russian missile bases and weapons in Cuba. President Kennedy ordered a "quarantine" or blockade of Cuba to prevent further weapons from being delivered and demanded the removal of the missile bases. Khrushchev finally ordered the missiles to be removed and the ships to return to the USSR. In return, the Americans removed some missiles from Turkey near the Russian border.

159. Indonesia

160. The United States, Russia, the United Kingdom, France, People's Republic of China, India, Pakistan, Israel

161. Challenges included ethnic strife; economic problems; lack of educated and experienced African leadership; and the lure of communism, which had an anti-imperialist stance.

162. The Mau Mau was a secret Kikuyu society dedicated to Kenyan nationalism. It eventually committed terrorist acts, particularly against white settlers. The government reacted with force and was able to suppress the movement between 1951 and 1952, but it was very costly.

163. Hungarians rose in rebellion against Soviet control. They wanted a higher standard of living, the withdrawal of Soviet troops, and an

independent nation. The Soviet Union under Nikita Khrushchev sent in forces and smashed the rebellion.

164. Soviet Premier Nikita Khrushchev. He was demonstrating the USSR's commitment to maintaining their power base in controlling the Soviet satellites in eastern Europe.

165. Millions of people were humiliated, persecuted, jailed, or sentenced to death. Anyone considered a member of the "elite"—teachers, managers, intellectuals, professionals—was targeted. Many were made to work in labor camps in the country or in factories. This eliminated those in China most capable of modernizing the country and educating its citizens.

166. Ho Chi Minh (real name—Nguyen Sinh Cung)

167. With the completion of the Human Genome Project in 2001, scientists have a genetic map of the human body. The promise of this is that we might be able to cure certain genetic diseases. The pitfall is the moral issue of whether or not we should be able to "custom-design" human beings.

168. Some of the companies students may list include Sony, Panasonic, JVC, Sanyo, Toshiba, and Mitsubishi.

169. 1(c); 2(d); 3(b); 4(e); 5(a)

170. Ayatollah Khomeini

171. Mikhail Gorbachev

172. He became Pope John Paul II.

173. East and West Germany were united as one country.

174. There was hostile world opinion and outcry againt the Chinese government for its crackdown on the protesters. A new set of Communist leaders took over and attempted to raise the standard of living for the Chinese people while remaining within an authorita-

tive political structure. China has become more open to the rest of the world economically and culturally since Tiananmen Square.

175. Nelson Mandela
176. Sarajevo, Bosnia
177. The European Economic Community has evolved into the European Union. The latest project of the EU was to formulate a common currency for EU members, the euro. The EU deals with more than just economic issues. It is working toward greater political unity for its member states.
178. OPEC—Organization of Petroleum Exporting Countries; GATT—General Agreement on Trade and Tariffs; IMF—International Monetary Fund; WTO—World Trade Organization
179. 1(a); 2(e); 3(d); 4(b); 5(c)
180. Al Qaeda: The aims of this group include overthrow of the Saudi Arabian royal family, destruction of the state of Israel, removal of the influence of the United States worldwide, and the ascendancy of fundamentalist Islamic groups. IRA: The Provisional Wing of the Irish Republican Army has used terrorism against the United Kingdom because they wish to see Northern Ireland unified with the Republic of Ireland. Hamas: A militant Palestinian Islamic movement in the West Bank and Gaza Strip, founded in 1987, it is dedicated to the destruction of Israel and the creation of an Islamic state in Palestine. Hamas opposes the 1993 peace accords between Israel and the Palestine Liberation Organization. Red Brigade: Active in Italy during the 1970s, they claimed to represent the masses against big business and the government. They used "knee-capping" (crippling people by shooting them in the kneecaps) as an instrument of terror and

assassinated an Italian prime minister. Black September: In the 1970s, this terrorist wing of the PLO killed 11 Israeli athletes at the Munich Olympic Games while millions of people watched on television. They wish the extermination of Israel.